SEROTONIN

SEROTONIN

IRVINE H. PAGE, M.D.

Director Emeritus, Research Division, Cleveland Clinic Foundation

YEAR BOOK MEDICAL PUBLISHERS · INC.

35 EAST WACKER DRIVE · CHICAGO

Preface

I THINK A READER IS ENTITLED to know the main reason why a book is written. Having been associated with serotonin from the beginning, I am assuming the right to express a point of view. There are already ample reviews and excellent books, large and extensively documented. What seems lacking is briefer and more intimate discussions by one or two authors, discussions that represent a single point of view to provide possible unity to a field that is becoming chaotic.

This is not by any means a comprehensive book. Some statements are made without even giving the reference, as should be done by any *proper* scientist. But the reader can pick up almost any trail from the selected references I have given. These references do not always indicate original discovery or even the best work; they are useful and readily available articles which often contain the pertinent bibliography. I have tried to avoid duplication of the earlier work that I have twice reviewed in *Physiological Reviews*.

In short, I have attempted to write a manuscript that will indicate what seem to me to be trends and highlights, so that a newcomer will not be overwhelmed by the thousands of papers already extant, too often uncorrelated with relevant physiological or pathological phenomena. I have tried to avoid the intellectual counterpart of the plight of the sorcerer's apprentice that might result if one inadvertently asked the computer for references on serotonin. This book has been written to be read, and in a short time at that!

Because this chapter in my life is closing, I choose to look back so that I may look forward with possibly some wisdom and hopefully some grace.

IRVINE H. PAGE

Contents

Introduction

It has been nearly 20 years since Rapport, Green and I isolated and identified serotonin from serum. The existence of this vasoconstrictor principle had been suspected for many years and was thought to be associated with blood coagulation, since such a substance appeared in serum but not in plasma. In the early thirties, Erspamer had made extracts of gastrointestinal tract which contracted smooth muscle, but there the subject remained. The subsequent history epitomizes a pattern of biomedical discovery. Clearly, serotonin has many functions but few have been sharply defined. The great variety of suggested roles can be said to be a tribute to man's ingenuity and his unquestionable willingness to write papers.

I repeat, it is not my purpose to document exhaustively, or even to discuss, many of the vast ramifications of the study of serotonin, as it has taken its place beside epinephrine and norepinephrine, histamine and acetylcholine. I have even omitted discussion of our own work on derivatives of serotonin such as 5-methoxy-N:N-dimethyltryptamine as a show of good faith to other authors. I have already written my share of reviews.[239, 240] The most recent and probably the best are those minor masterpieces of documentation, the books by Garattini and Valzelli,[135] Garattini, Shore, Costa and Sandler[134] and several reviews by Erspamer,[105, 107, 108] Carlsson,[61] Sjoerdsma,[306] Sollero,[314] Von Euler, Rosell and Uvnäs[112] and Giarman and Freedman.[144] Rather, I have preferred to be selective, according to my own light, and to stay within the limits of an overview of the subject.

The Changing Atmosphere of Discovery

As has often been true of other substances of wide interest, the circumstances of the discovery of serotonin are hazy to most people. The changes that have occurred in operational methods of science in the United States are such that now *one* man seldom makes a discovery.

Physiologists had known for many years that when blood coagulates it takes on vasoconstrictor properties. As one concerned as early as 1928 with the problem of whether hypertension was due to vasoconstrictors in the blood, I was preoccupied with this fact. In principle, it could be that whenever blood is drawn the demonstration of a vasoconstrictor substance by pharmacological means merely proves again this long-recognized phenomenon. In 1930, Hessel, one of Volhard's students, introduced me to renin, which was suggested as the humoral pressor agent responsible for hypertension. But renin had not been isolated from blood nor indeed from kidney, its source. I started on the problem of identifying renin in blood of dogs with experimental renal hypertension and by 1934 I fully comprehended that the *serum vasoconstrictor* had to be understood as a prelude to the search for a plasma vasoconstrictor of renal origin. I turned to perfusion of rabbit's ear vessels as economic—remember, this was during the Great Depression—if only because there are two ears, rather than the one dog's tail used by my colleague, Kohlstaedt, to assay the steps in our purification of renin. This technique, though useful, had serious drawbacks. Indeed, in the eyes of Landis, Wood and Guerrant,[193] these were so serious as largely to negate the value

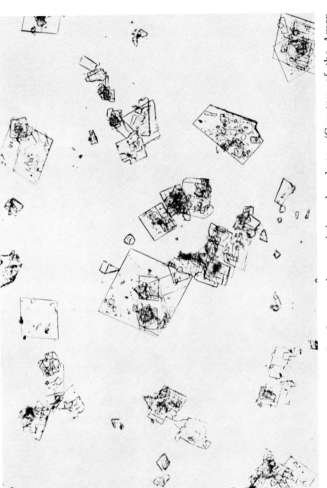

Fig. 1.—Original crystals of serotonin creatinine phosphate. (Courtesy of the American Heart Journal 38:161, 1949.)

of our work. But certain facts and ideas about the nature of serum vasoconstrictor were nonetheless obtained. I later formed a team with Drs. Arda Green and Maurice Rapport to pursue the matter further when we came to Cleveland. A series of papers followed[266, 267, 268, 269] in which the isolation, crystallization and almost complete characterization of structure were documented. The last report on the final structure was made by Rapport alone in 1949, after which he left the field. We were totally unaware of any relationship of this substance we called *serotonin* to the uterus-contracting material contained in extracts of stomach and intestine discovered by Erspamer and Vialli in 1937. They did not isolate, nor identify, this material but called the active substance in the extracts "enteramine." In 1952, Erspamer and Asero[109] showed by chemical means that it was identical with our serotonin. By any standards, Erspamer must be recognized as one of the most productive and gifted investigators in the field.

Gaddum introduced the curiously inconsistent abbreviation system, referring to the substance as 5-HT or HT. Thus, serotonin became 5-HT while melatonin, choline and histamine remain pleasant contributions to our language. I suspect we lose something when discovery is promptly shorn of its personal aspects and appears merely as an abbreviation. Somehow, 5-HT seems stark and forlorn, serotonin and melatonin mellifluous and warm. If I were a student, the former would not fire my imagination. But then, I have never favored the free use of arbitrary abbreviations. The latest oddity is 5 HT'01, which most people not thoroughly familiar with the field would hardly guess represented 5-hydroxytryptophol.

Perhaps it is old-fashioned to memorize science by associating discoveries with people. Perhaps all scientists should be nameless and faceless, but I sincerely hope not in my time. In my view, there is nothing like them; which may be just as well!

The Effects of Availability

Serotonin quickly became available in large quantities thanks to its synthesis by Hamlin and Fischer.[161] To promote diverse types of research, no single step is more important than having a new substance available. In this, the pharmaceutical companies, especially Abbott Laboratories of Chicago and later the Upjohn Company of Kalamazoo, Michigan, have played an invaluable part. Within months, a flood of studies began to appear and today, some 20 years later, it has not ebbed. The original workers can no longer keep a rein on the many ramifications and both inevitably, and rightly, leadership is taken over by others. What occurred in the case of serotonin?

A group guided by the greatly skilled Sidney Udenfriend and Albert Sjoerdsma undertook the analysis of the chemical mechanisms for the biosynthesis and destruction of serotonin. Erspamer largely studied the natural occurrence of serotonin and other indole alkylamines. He has continued to show his genius by characterizing other substances of widely differing chemical nature. Brodie showed the great importance of storage and release with his demonstration with Pletscher and Shore that reserpine depletes the stores, especially in brain. Woolley and Shaw have been the most vocal proponents of the participation of serotonin in the metabolism of brain. Arvid Carlsson, Hillarp and their many gifted associates have added immeasurably to knowledge of the pharmacology and distribution of serotonin. But the area of the physiology and pharmacology is so vast and so many have contributed to it that it is impossible to make proper attribution. Suffice it to say that McCubbin and I noted that serotonin had replaced epinephrine as a sure road to *tenure* for the pharmacologist.[242]

A large amount of work was initiated after the studies of Biörck, Thorson and Waldenström on the secretion of serotonin by carcinoid tumors. Lastly, many pharmaceutical firms put much effort into developing serotonin antagonists. Thus, the past 20 years have been extraordinarily productive, resulting in thousands of papers, and even a great deal of extraordinarily valuable information. It is time to evaluate this work because much raw experimental data are now available. This period of naturalistic gathering of observations was necessary to provide a base for more disciplined and ordered studies.

CHAPTER 1

Certain Aspects of the Biochemistry of Serotonin

The Distribution of a Chemical

THE DISTRIBUTION OF a substance or a disease, whether endogenous or exogenous in relation to the body, often hints at the function of the substance or the causes of the disease.

Erspamer and Vialli found a uterus-contracting material in the enterochromaffin cells of the gastrointestinal tract; after formalin fixation, the presence of chromaffin or argentaffin granules capable of coupling with diazonium salts was demonstrable. They had a characteristic fluorescence in Wood's light. The term "enterochromaffin" later proved to be too restrictive because chromaffin cells occur in places other than the gastrointestinal tract, such as the posterior salivary glands of the octopus, in amphibian cutaneous glands and in the poison-gland cells of some coelenterates. Mast cells of some animals, notably rats and mice, contain serotonin. By their beautiful fluorescence techniques, Falck and Hillarp have demonstrated that serotonin is widespread in the body. Serotonin increases in the allantoic fluid of chick embryos between the ninth and twelfth days as well as other tryptophan metabolites such as kynuremic and xanthurenic acids, according to Boucek, Boucek, Hlavackova and Dietrich.[45] Since Falck and Owman[115] have recently so capably reviewed the

15

localization of serotonin in endocrine cell systems, there is no need to repeat it here.

Aside from the enterochromaffin cells, endogenous serotonin is found chiefly in platelets and in nervous tissue. Mast cells of some species contain both it and histamine. Its occurrence in cells closely associated with the gastrointestinal tract led to the suggestion that it controlled intestinal propulsion, at least in part. Its presence in platelets led to several postulates concerning its function, the most common being an association with hemostasis. Further, platelets were thought to be a source of serotonin concerned in cardiovascular regulation. I have likened platelets to the synaptic vesicles at nerve endings in the brain, since they both take up and release serotonin, a similarity seen in the uptake and release of catecholamines.

Robertson and Andrews[277] have measured free serotonin in human plasma with Vane's excellent method using fundal strip of rat's stomach. In four patients with carcinoid and normal platelet counts, the venous level was between 20 and 60 ng/ml. However, a fifth patient with carcinoid and thrombocytopenia had levels less than 10 ng/ml. Many doubt that free serotonin exists in normal plasma, at least as measured by current methods.

Twarog and I,[336] much to our surprise, first showed serotonin to be present in *brain,* chiefly I suppose, because Doctor Twarog knew how to prepare for study the heart of the mollusc, *Venus mercenaria.* It turned out to be a sensitive and selective method for measuring serotonin. Serotonin in brain was systematically studied the following year by Amin, Crawford and Gaddum.[4] First identification of serotonin in brain by chemical methods was by Bogdanski, Pletscher, Brodie and Udenfriend.[40] Newer studies show the pineal region to be especially rich in it in both the parenchymal cells and in the pineal sympathetic nerves (Bertler, Falck and Owman[33]). The significance of its occurrence in brain has been highly controversial chiefly because if serotonin could be causally associated with mentation or transmission, its importance would be enormous.

I have not the competence to give a proper discussion of the anatomy of serotonergic neurons. Fortunately, Hillarp, Fuxe and Dahlström have recently published a discussion of the problem.[170] In short, they find these cells mainly in the lower brain stem and quite differently localized from the adrenergic fibers. The mesencephalon is very rich in them. Their terminals mainly innervate afferent and efferent nuclei of the cranial nerves. Contrasting with the adrenergic terminals, which contact both catecholamine and serotonin-containing nerve cell bodies, the serotonergic terminals touch only cells which do not contain monoamines. Descending monoaminergic nerve tracts have been demonstrated in the spinal cord (Carlsson, Falck, Fuxe and Hillarp[66]). The cell bodies are in the brain stem and the terminals are highly concentrated in the sympathetic lateral columns. In mice, these pathways dominate quantitatively over those containing norepinephrine.

The time of appearance of serotonin in the developing brain has been associated by Karki, Kuntzman and Brodie[184] with the subcortical behavior of animals. Newborn rats and rabbits are helpless and, correspondingly, lack the biochemical mechanisms for synthesis and storage of cerebral amines. But, as they develop behavioral patterns, the amine levels rise for about three weeks. In contrast, the guinea pig which has well-developed patterns at birth also has the capacity to metabolize these amines. Bennett and Giarman[31] found the major increase in rat cerebral serotonin and monoamine oxidase activity occurred after birth while 5-hydroxytryptophan decarboxylase approached adult levels at birth. The ability of young rat brain to synthesize serotonin from blood-borne L-5-hydroxytryptophan was the same in newborn and adult. Since synthesis of serotonin from L-tryptophan was greatly reduced, the lower level of brain serotonin was probably due to reduced capacity to hydroxylate tryptophan.

The high-speed centrifuge residues of rat brain contain more than 70 per cent of the total cerebral serotonin of rats at all ages (Haber and Kamano[156]).

Brodie, Bogdanski and Bonomi[48] found serotonin present in brain of all vertebrate classes. In *reptilia* and *amphibia,* its concentration is high in comparison with mammals, and exceptionally high in toads. In fish, it is lower than in mammals. Brodie and Costa[50] suggested that in contrast with norepinephrine, which they believe *integrates* sympathetic activity with somatomotor activities to produce patterns of behavior which require energy, serotonin *integrates* parasympathetic with somatomotor activities to form recuperative and protective behavioral patterns. The occurrence of both serotonin and norepinephrine in brain of all vertebrates, along with these mutually antagonistic systems originally described by Hess, suggests a long phylogenetic history.

The brains of 16 North American reptiles were analyzed for serotonin by Quay and Wilhoft.[265] Whole brain content exhibited an inverse relationship between animal size and serotonin content. Thus, the lowest content was found in alligator brain. The concentrations in different regions of brain were similar to those found in mammals and birds. The lowest content usually occurred in olfactory bulbs, cerebellum and the highest in some parts of the brain stem. In reptiles, the highest was found in the mesencephalic tegmentum. The reptile that shows great similarity to mammals in both absolute and relative levels of serotonin in brain is the alligator, a species representing a phylogenetically highly distinctive group.

The highest concentrations of both serotonin and norepinephrine are found in phyletically older structures, which indicates their association with autonomic functions and the integration of emotional patterns.[259] The variations within reptiles suggests that studies of the function of cerebral serotonin might be rewarding in these and other poikilotherms in comparison with mammals whose brain temperatures may be expected to induce narrower operational ranges.

Serotonin is widespread among the lower animals (Welsh and Moorhead[352]). It inhibits the action of Limulus hearts (Burgen and Kuffler[58]) but excites crustacean hearts (Florey and Florey[123]). The odd distribution of serotonin in the vegetable and lower animal world has led to two quite disparate theories: (1) that its presence, for example, in stinging nettle and the nematocysts of Hydra, constitutes a defense system because it is strongly algogenic—a nice word meaning *to produce pain*—a system which carries over into lower animals and (2) that the consumption of large quantities of serotonin-containing foods, such as bananas, or walnuts, possibly leads to development of endomyocardial fibrosis in men. The high content of serotonin in banana skin possibly is associated with its psychedelic action when smoked by some of our younger generation. Serotonin is so curiously distributed that it is currently unreasonable to expect a unifying concept of its function or functions to be derived from this knowledge.

Most students accept the view that the serotonin and its derivatives in the nervous system function quite differently from that in the rest of the body and that little of the somatic serotonin penetrates the brain.

On one aspect there is general agreement—wherever there is autonomic activity, serotonin is usually present in serotonergic neurons. Similarly, the indolealkylamines are richly populated with substances that disturb mentation, and from this derives the intriguing idea that somehow these substances are concerned with mental disease.

The distribution of serotonin in the gastrointestinal tract and in platelets has provided the basis for the working hypothesis that it is concerned in peristalsis, coagulation and regulation of the circulation.

These, then, are the broad outlines of what has been

learned from studying the distribution of serotonin. Clearly, this outline needs fleshing out!

Methods for Its Determination

The presence of a biologically active substance in extracts of tissue as measured by its contracting effect on smooth muscle was the first clue to serotonin's presence. This shows again the great importance of vertebrate intestine and of uterus as guides to the existence of vasoactive materials. This has applied to vasoactive peptides as well as to amines.

One of the most useful specialized tissue additions has been the determination of serotonin and its analogs by the rat's stomach strip—Vane's method.[345] The molluscan heart and Byssus retractor muscle of clams have also proved their usefulness in bioanalysis (Twarog[335]). Still another is the assay of the central action of serotonin by the head-twitch response of mice following injection of 5-hydroxytryptophan. Corne, Pickering and Warner[79] have used it successfully in screening for compounds likely to have central actions.

The fact that many indoles exhibit intense fluorescence was early utilized by Bowman and Udenfriend to develop methods of assay of great sensitivity and specificity. Indeed, this led Udenfriend to write a highly significant book on the relationship of fluorescence to chemical structure. Chromatography has also come into routine use to isolate and identify indoles. As has so often proved true recently, this method has had an extraordinary influence on problems concerned with the isolation of *new* substances. Their separation seems so relatively easy today in contrast to 30 years ago, when countercurrent distribution and chromatography were unknown. These have replaced the hand-shaken separatory funnel, the one-time hallmark of the biochemist. The younger generation will never appreciate how hard it was to purify, or to isolate, a substance before the advent of these newer methods.

Following Falck and Hillarp, a variety of histochemical fluorescence methods have been widely used,[131] especially by the Swedish groups of workers in Göteborg and Stockholm.

Two different fluorimetric methods are used for the determination of serotonin in tissues, the one of Bogdanski, Pletscher, Brodie and Udenfriend[40] based on measurement of the fluorescence of serotonin in 3 N HCl and the other on its reaction with ninhydrin (Vanable[343]; Snyder, Axelrod and Zweig[312]). One of the difficulties is that the tissue blank is unreliable when the serotonin content is low. Andén and Magnusson[10] noted that certain batches of concentrated HCl containing Fe^{+++}-ion as impurity caused rapid destruction of serotonin by the activation light in the spectrophotofluorimeter. From this, they developed a method for obtaining reliable blanks.

The fluorescence is read in 3 N HCl and the tissue blank produced by means of UV-irradiation in presence of potassium ferricyanide, so destroying only the serotonin. Using this new type of blank and reducing the volumes of the eluate and the reagents, the sensitivity of the method was improved so that 25 ng in an extract is demonstrable and 50 ng is measurable quantitatively. The stability of the serotonin in the perchloric acid extract was also increased by adjustment of the pH almost to neutrality and by addition of ascorbic acid and ethylenediamine tetra-acetate.

Perhaps the most important lesson learned from attempts to measure indolealkylamines is that they may be present in such minute amounts, changes in levels may easily be missed and turnover rates could only be measured after introduction of radioactive tagging. Further, it has become clear that we are only at the threshold of understanding how this great family of substances functions in the body. Many tantalizing bits of information *suggest* vitally important mechanisms. Refinement of methods for measurement of the various serotonin derivatives is essential to dispel current uncertainty.

The Biosynthesis of Serotonin

Blaschko in 1952 suggested that the natural substrate for tryptophan decarboxylase was 5-hydroxytryptophan and the next year Udenfriend, Clark and Titus[338] separated the enzyme from kidney. 5-Hydroxytryptophan decarboxylase appeared to be the same enzyme as dopa decarboxylase found in 1938 by Holtz, Heise and Lüdtke. Pyridoxal phosphate acts as coenzyme.

It is helpful to know the distribution of such an enzyme if only to estimate the potentiality for serotonin formation. Its greatest activity is in kidneys; there is much less in liver and gut but substantial amounts in nerve tissue, especially sympathetic ganglia and adrenal medulla (Gaddum and Giarman[132]). Bone marrow and platelets have none. Clearly, the distribution of 5-hydroxytryptophan decarboxylase does not coincide either with the tissue content of serotonin or the idea that most extracerebral serotonin synthesis occurs in the enterochromaffin cells of the gut.

In disease, the pheochromocytoma and neoplastic mast cells of mice have rich supplies. This might be expected if the enzyme functions primarily as a dopa decarboxylase.

At the time of discovery of 5-hydroxytryptophan decarboxylase its role was believed to be a critical one in rate limiting the formation of serotonin. Udenfriend, Bogdanski and Weissbach[337, 340] had made the interesting observation that feeding 5-hydroxytryptophan caused an increase in serotonin content of tissues, including brain, indicating the activity of the decarboxylating enzyme.

In 1958, Bogdanski, Weissbach and Udenfriend[41] showed the functional effects of infusion of 5-hydroxytryptophan on the whole animal. Unlike serotonin, this amino acid rapidly penetrates most tissues and is converted to serotonin by the decarboxylase. Iproniazid potentiated the cerebral effects by inhibiting the destruction of serotonin.

Dogs and cats exhibited an extraordinary series of behavioral changes, especially after blockade of monoamine oxidase. At first, they appeared sedated but, as serotonin built up in the brain, they became greatly excited, ataxic, seemed blind, disoriented and unresponsive to auditory and visual stimuli. These responses grossly simulate those which result from the action of LSD despite qualitative and quantitative differences. Chlorpromazine largely prevented the effects. In man, very much smaller doses of the amino acid resulted in nausea and increase in intraluminal intestinal pressure with cramps, which sharply limited the amount that could be given.

Changes in mood and social behavior have been observed by Smith and Prockop[310] following ingestion of 30, 50, 70 and 90 ng of L-tryptophan per kilogram body weight on successive days in normal human beings. The effects were proportional to the amount of amino acid given and were reproducible. The so-called "toxicity" of L-tryptophan and other amino acids needs further study.

I have confirmed Udenfriend's work in a large series of experiments on unanesthetized dogs. In addition, I found that the infusion of 5-hydroxytryptophan reversed the pressor response of injected serotonin to depressor and that the syndrome was not due to liberation of catecholamines. If the infusion of the amino acid was continued, arterial pressure fell and the animal died.

These experiments show the results of change in serotonin content of tissues made possible because the amino acid has a high degree of cellular penetrance, especially in brain, not shared by serotonin itself. If the term *hallucination* may be applied to animals, the physical manifestations strongly suggested this mental derangement. I am much reminded of alcoholic hallucinations or Korsakoff syndrome in man, even to the accompanying vocalization.

There can be no doubt that marked changes in serotonin content of brain due to synthesis and degradation are associated with pronounced changes in mentation. Whether these have any mechanistic relationship is not known. Some of the methylated derivatives of serotonin, notably N,N-dimethyltryptamine, show similar cerebral actions.

This evidence reiterates, as so resolutely pointed out over the years by Woolley, that the analysis of the participation of the indolealkylamines in cerebral metabolism is likely to be highly rewarding. I have failed currently to find any long-range, broadly based program of this kind, although the need is great.

One of the most productive studies on 5-hydroxytryptophan decarboxylase was the finding by Sourkes in 1954 that 3,4-dihydroxy-alpha-methyl-phenylalanine (alpha-methyldopa) synthesized by Karl Pfister, was a powerful inhibitor, the inhibition not being due to complexing with pyridoxal phosphate. In the hands of Sjoerdsma, Udenfriend and their colleagues this became a valuable, widely used, antihypertensive agent. By an odd twist of fate, its ability to lower blood pressure has turned out to be not primarily due to its inhibitory effect on decarboxylase.

In vitro hydroxylation of tryptophan to 5-hydroxytryptophan occurs in rat liver and intestinal mucosa and was shown by Renson, Weissbach and Udenfriend[274] to be due to phenylalanine hydroxylase. Gal and Marshall[133] demonstrated that radioactive tryptophan injected into the subarachnoid space was hydroxylated to 5-hydroxytryptophan. But there is good evidence that phenylalanine hydroxylase is not the major catalyst of the hydroxylation of tryptophan. Indeed, in 1958 Udenfriend stated that tryptophan is not converted to 5-hydroxytryptophan by any known hydroxylating system, including phenylalanine hydroxylase. But the venom-producing glands of toads contain a 5-hydroxylating enzyme. Curiously, a tryptophan hydroxylase was also found in a bacterium *Chromobacterium violaceum*.

It is not certainly known where serotonin is synthesized in neurons but by analogy synthesis probably occurs in the cell body. Dahlström[89] has presented strong evidence that catecholamines behave similarly. She found the storage granules transported down the axon to the terminals at a rate of about 5 mm/hour in rats and 100 mm in cats. Some sort of peristaltic activity in the axon membrane or Schwann cells seems to cause the movement. The life span of the granules in the terminals was calculated to be about 35 days in rats and 70 days in cats. An interesting finding was that the time required for the total recovery of the norepinephrine levels after reserpine was shown to be about the same as the calculated life span of the amine granules, suggesting that reserpine blocks the storage mechanism in the granules irreversibly. The increase in tissue norepinephrine after reserpine-depletion is, then, due to donor transport of newly formed amine storage granules.

5-Hydroxylation of Tryptophan in Brain

Hydroxylation of tryptophan in the five position is the first and probably the rate-limiting reaction in the formation of serotonin. Grahame-Smith[147] found that brain homogenates were able to hydroxylate tryptophan, and Weber and Horita[349] indirectly showed the same is true *in vivo* by measuring the synthesis of serotonin from tryptophan infused into the brain.

There has been much uncertainty as to whether a highly specific hydroxylase exists in brain, but with the development by Lovenberg, Jequier and Sjoerdsma[197] of a sensitive radioassay, the conversion of tryptophan to 5-hydroxytryptophan showed the presence of this enzyme in a variety of tissues. Beef and rat pineal tissue contained the highest activity; rat and rabbit brain stem, mouse mast cell tumors and human carcinoid cells and platelets all showed easily measurable amounts. The reaction requires reduced pteridine and oxygen and is inhibited by p-chlorophenylalanine. The latter specific serotonin depleter (Koe and Weissman[185]), when given to rats, also inhibits the hydroxylase.

Jequier, Lovenberg and Sjoerdsma[178] correlated the enzyme inhibition with cerebral serotonin depletion, presumably this being the cause. p-Chlorophenylalanine is a competitive inhibitor *in vitro* but causes irreversible inhibition *in vivo*. The parallelism between the serotonin content and tryptophan hydroxylase activity in brain after administration of p-chlorophenylalanine suggests that cerebral serotonin results from the action of tryptophan hydroxylase within the brain. The parallelism also is evidence that tryptophan hydroxylation is the rate-limiting enzymatic step in serotonin biosynthesis. The enzyme does not normally appear to be fully saturated with substrate; hence, the rate of synthesis of serotonin may be partially dependent upon the availability of tryptophan.

Rat pineal cells in culture have been used by Shein, Wurtman and Axelrod[304] to study the synthesis of serotonin from both tryptophan and 5-hydroxytryptophan. Their data indicate clearly that the activity of the decarboxylase is much greater than that of the hydroxylating enzyme and that the latter is rate-limiting for formation of serotonin.

The striking similarity between the enzymatic systems responsible for synthesis and degradation of serotonin and those for the catecholamines is clear. Tryptophan and tyrosine hydroxylase seem to be much alike. Their distribution in the body is not the same, suggesting that the need for serotonin occurs in places different from catecholamines. But, like the catecholamines, serotonin synthesis can only be greatly reduced at the level of 5-hydroxylation of the amino acid and its degradation can be slowed by amine oxidase inhibitors.

Alpha-methyl-p-tyrosine and its methyl ester inhibit tyrosine hydroxylase effectively (Spector, Sjoerdsma and Udenfriend[317]). This shows the difference from tryptophan hydroxylase since Andén, Corrodi, Dahlström, Fuxe and Hökfelt[5] found the methyl ester does not affect the serotonin levels of rat's brain or spinal cord. There was no difference among the various regions in rate and degree of depletion of the terminals and cell bodies.

Udenfriend and Witkop described an interesting intramolecular migration during the hydroxylation of tryptophan and other aromatic compounds. Thus, 5-tritiotryptophan is converted by the enzyme tryptophan-5-hydroxylase to 5-hydroxy-4-tritiotryptophan. The tritium shows great lability in the enzymatically produced 5-hydroxytryptophan. This reaction has been called the "NIH shift" and appears to be a fundamental property of aromatic hydroxylation reactions[152, 273] (Fig. 2).

Uptake and Storage

C^{14}-serotonin injected intravenously into mice was found by Axelrod and Inscoe[20] to disappear in two phases. In the first few minutes about half is metabolized, presumably by enzymatic deamination. This is followed by the second phase, a gradual fall over many days. A striking aspect is its uptake and prolonged retention by special tissues and, since approximately half is bound in the first few minutes, this mechanism becomes a major one in terminating the action of circulating serotonin. Spleen and lung are unusually active in this regard and yet both contain large amounts of endogenous amine. Intestine, while containing large amounts, takes up relatively little.

Fig. 2.—Action of tryptophan-5-hydroxylase on 5-tritiotryptophan. (Courtesy of G. Guroff, J. W. Daly, D. M. Jerina, J. Renson, B. Witkop and S. Udenfriend: Science 157:1524, 1967.)

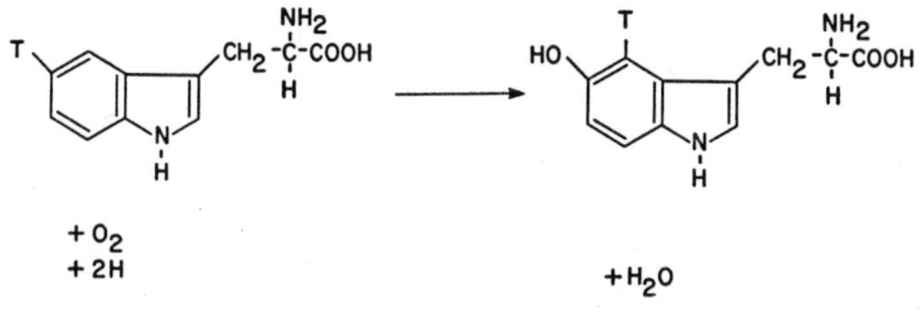

Erspamer[106] had shown that serotonin injected subcutaneously into rats is slowly absorbed; after 3 hours, 7.5 per cent of the original remained. After either subcutaneous or intraperitoneal administration, the plasma level rises. If the platelet level of serotonin is measured as the difference between that of serum and plasma, it rises after a subcutaneous injection of 25 mg/kg to a maximum after about 5 hours to about 260 per cent of the usual content, and in the following 5 hours about 25 per cent of it is lost. It must be recognized that this is only a rough approximation because of many unknown factors involved. If platelets selectively concentrate circulating serotonin, as shown by Zucker and Borrelli,[364] and since both lung and spleen remove platelets, it has been suggested that the relatively high concentration in these organs may be due to platelet entrapment. Axelrod and Inscoe[20] believe this unlikely, since platelets take up less than 1 per cent of administered serotonin. This is in sharp contrast with the finding of selective concentration.

Since platelets lack the enzymatic mechanisms for synthesis of serotonin (Gaddum and Giarman[132]) and Zucker found none in newly formed ones, it is probable that they take up at least a small amount of free serotonin in plasma. According to Stacey,[319] platelets contain almost all of the blood serotonin, negligible amounts being extractable from red and white cells. But, in most storage cells other than platelets, decarboxylation of the amino acid occurs within the cytoplasm and from there serotonin enters storage granules.

Serotonin is also taken up and retained for relatively long periods by uterus and heart. Reserpine but not LSD or compound 48/80 releases the bound C^{14}-serotonin from uterus and spleen (Snyder, Axelrod, Wurtman and Fisher[311]).

It was found by Humphrey and Toh[174] and Hardisty and Stacey[163] that platelets take serotonin up *in vitro*. The remarkably high content of ATP found in platelets by Born,[43] in enterochromaffin granules (Prusoff[258]) and adrenal medullary chromaffin granules (Blaschko, Born, D'Iorio and

Eade[37]) suggested that uptake might be an energy-consuming process, as is its release (Born, Ingram and Stacey[44]).

Starling and Verney[321] first noted that the vasoconstrictor activity of shed blood was removed by perfusion through the lungs of a dog. The liver also removed serotonin. Recently, the relative importance of platelet, lung, liver and peripheral vascular bed as site of uptake in dogs anesthetized with chloralose was carefully studied by Thomas and Vane.[329] They used a continuous assay method in which blood bathes a rat stomach strip and rat colon. The former responds to serotonin and the latter to angiotensin and prostaglandins. Platelets, as had formerly been thought by some, did not account for the rapid disappearance of infused serotonin. When infused into the portal vein, about 70 per cent disappeared before reaching the heart. The rate was remarkably constant from dog to dog; up to the highest rate of infusion tested (400 μg/min) the same percentage disappeared. More than 90 per cent disappeared in the pulmonary circulation. The percentage removed was not changed by blocking monoamine oxidase with nialamide.

That blockade was accomplished was shown by prolonging the pressor action of tyramine. The percentage of serotonin disappearing during perfusion of peripheral vascular beds varied from 30 to 60. Thus, the lungs seem to be the chief site of removal, with the liver next in importance. These two vascular beds should prevent most of the serotonin from reaching the arterial circulation. Epinephrine, in contrast, seems to pass through the lung without loss.

As Gershon and Ross[141] showed, serotonin is specifically taken up among several tissues by the reticuloendothelial cells in the liver and septal cells in the lungs.

Since serotonin does not pass the blood-brain barrier, the device of injecting it directly into the cerebral ventricles has been used to increase the cerebral content. Some evidence suggests (Aghajanian, Bloom, Lovell, Sheard and Freedman[1]) that part of it is taken up by the choroid plexus (Tochino and Schanker[332]). Tritiated serotonin injected into rats' ventricles is retained 4 hours or more. It was found in the hypothalamus and within the neurophils adjacent to the ventricles. The intense peridendritic autoradiographic activity strongly suggests localization in the nerve terminals.

It was noted in 1954 by De Robertis and Bennett[93] that the nerve synapses contain vesicles about 500 Å wide, remarkably uniform in size, which they designated "synaptic vesicles." Whittaker[355] showed these could be isolated from brain by gradient centrifugation, so providing an unusually useful preparation for the study of neurohumors. Serotonin has been found concentrated in this vesicle fraction, suggesting their similarity with blood platelets. For those interested in this important aspect of biogenic amines and enzymes of the gamma-aminobutyric acid system as well, I can strongly recommend a recent discussion by De Robertis.[92]

Palaić, Page and Khairallah[245] determined the amount of labeled serotonin and 5-hydroxyindoleacetic acid after perfusing rat's brain ventricles with labeled serotonin, finding that it was taken up at a rate greater than the accumulation of radioactivity in the brain itself. It was assumed that the excess serotonin was removed by the choroid plexus. The cerebral intracellular serotonin increased the 5-hydroxyindole acetic acid during the first hour of perfusion but not during the second; hence, it was postulated that the labeled serotonin taken up increased the content of endogenous serotonin, in part, by saturating monoamine oxidase. Ouabain, norepinephrine, reserpine, but not desmethylimipramine, significantly decreased serotonin uptake, suggesting an active transport mechanism. The behavioral effects of intraventricular serotonin have been described in detail by Feldberg.[117]

Gershon and Ross[140] studied the distribution of serotonin synthesized *in vivo* from administered tritium-labeled 5-hydroxytryptophan. Serotonin was taken up rapidly and retained for long periods by adrenal medullary and gastric enterochromaffin cells, blood platelets, thyroid parafollicular cells, beta cells of pancreatic islets, mast cells and septal cells of the lung. Reticuloendothelial cells of liver and spleen took it up more slowly but also retained it for days. Specific uptake and rapid turnover was found in pancreatic exocrine cells, renal proximal tubular cells, neurons of the superior cervical ganglion, terminal axons of gastrointestinal myenteric plexus, carotid body cells and pinealocytes. This broad and variable uptake of endogenous serotonin is both surprising and disappointing to me because it fails to give the expected clues as to possible functions of serotonin.

Autoradiographic study of the distribution in mice of the tagged precursor of serotonin, 5-hydroxytryptophan (Ritzén, Hammarström and Ullberg[276]) showed the radioactivity initially accumulated in the pancreas and other organs characterized by rapid protein synthesis. Within about 4 hours, the immediate distribution pattern was replaced by one in which localization occurred in adrenal medulla, thyroid, islands of Langerhans, bone marrow, red pulp of spleen and lung. Thus, the precursor of serotonin does not distribute itself in any more understandable pattern than serotonin itself. It is, however, similar to that observed with C^{14} dopa.

While injected serotonin concentrated in bone marrow and spleen, as well as the myocardium, the amount decreased rapidly. Reticuloendothelial cells of liver and spleen acquired it more slowly but retained it for days. The binding of the serotonin in tissues was so strong that they can be washed in physiological saline before fixation without changing its localization.

The usual idea of storage is that the enterochromaffin cells, the platelets and the brain—more especially areas of autonomic function—are the only important ones. It was relatively so much simpler when we could believe this. Storage in lower animals is so bizarre as to defy any association with function. Thus, amphibian skin, venoms of some molluscs, scorpions, coelenterates and insects and posterior salivary glands, seem to be storehouses of indolealkylamines as well as vasoactive polypeptides. Then a whole series of plants, including banana, pineapple, plantain and walnuts, were found to contain large amounts. Another curious fact is that mast cells of rats and mice contain serotonin while those of most other mammals do not! Serotonin is correspondingly abundant in mast cells of mice with either mastocytomas or mast cell leukemia. It seems to be synthesized by these cells, since neoplastic mast cells still contain serotonin after many generations in cell cultures.

Release

For the past several years there has been much interest in the mechanisms of release of biogenic amines. Carlsson[62] suggests that there is an "internal" and "external" release induced by drugs. The internal appears to be caused by blockade of granule storage (reserpine, tetrabenazine and prenylamine): external release requires the combined blockade of granule storage and membrane pump (tyramine, guanethidine, monoamine oxidase inhibitors alone or followed by reserpine). But these are only two of several mechanisms concerned in release. But first consider some of the functional relationships concerned in release.

Since mast cells tend to be in juxtaposition to blood vessels, it is natural to believe that their content of vasoactive histamine and serotonin is secreted to act on these vessels.

Serotonin released from the enterochromaffin cells into the portal blood possibly is absorbed by platelets (Erspamer[106]). Seemingly for this reason, platelet serotonin falls sharply after partial removal of the gastrointestinal tract in both man and animals (Haverback[165]), indicating that this is a most important source of the amine.

Also, the theme of the relationship between serotonin and connective tissue appears in many and varied garbs. Endomyocardial fibrosis in the carcinoid syndrome is one of the most striking examples. Since connective tissue formation is invariably initiated by an accumulation of mast cells believed to produce important ground substance components, the effects of serotonin were studied. Asboe-Hansen and Wegelius[17] noted pronounced edema of the connective tissue as well as mast cell degranulation in the cheek pouch of hamsters within 10 to 20 minutes following intraperitoneal injection of serotonin. The mast cells, however, were left intact. They believe that serotonin release has a function in connective tissue repair and regeneration. In the same year, Rowley and Benditt[283] suggested serotonin as a mediator of the local vascular injury with edema formation produced by agents such as ovomucoid, compound 48/80 and dextran, which degranulate mast cells in rats.

When injected subcutaneously, both tryptamine and 5-hydroxytryptamine produced edema and increased capillary permeability, but serotonin was 10 times the more potent. Specific antihistaminic agents such as pyrilamine did not inhibit edema so elicited. The released serotonin, possibly in conjunction with histamine from mast cells, appears to mediate the edema and increased vascular permeability. These phenomena seem to be species-limited because Parratt and West[249] failed to find serotonin concentrated in tissue mast cells of guinea pig, dog, man, rabbit, cow, hamster and cat. In contrast, these cells in rats and mice contain large quantities.

Bhattacharya and Lewis[34] found no evidence for release of serotonin by compound 48/80 from perfused tissue of cat, dog and rabbit, but in contrast it released histamine and serotonin from perfused rat's tissues. This emphasizes that serotonin is not a constituent of the mast cells of all species. They concluded that serotonin appearing after injection of histamine liberators like the released histamine and heparin, originates in the mast cells. Reserpine depletes the mast cells in the tissues of rat's hind quarters of serotonin without affecting their histamine content (Bhattacharya and Lewis[35]).

The relatively recent beautiful studies by Moran, Uvnäs and Westerholm[223] have done much to reactivate interest in mechanisms of release. Uvnäs[342] showed that phospholipase A initiates but does not complete the release of serotonin from rat's peritoneal mast cells. Glucose can provide the necessary energy for the reaction. Further studies by Moran, Uvnäs and Westerholm strongly suggest that the enzymatic mechanism for polymer-induced (i.e., compound 48/80) release of serotonin is the same as that for the release of histamine. Compound 48/80 was used as a model releasing agent because the pattern of its release of histamine is similar to that by antigen. A variety of unrelated substances cause release of serotonin and histamine from mast cells, among them propamidine, toluidine blue, morphine, polymyxin B, dextran, egg white and extracts of some tissues. Allicin, ninhydrin and dinitrophenol in a glucose-free medicine inhibit serotonin release while sodium cyanide and anoxia do not.

Reserpine released neither serotonin nor histamine from rat's peritoneal mast cells *in vitro* (Moran and Westerholm[224]), although *in vivo* there was some reduction in content. It seemed to affect other tissues of rats differently, causing sharp reduction of serotonin in brain but little in skin, ileum, duodenum, pylorus or fundus. In contrast, pretreatment with compound 48/80 caused disappearance of all mast cells, serotonin and histamine from peritoneal fluid. Clearly, reserpine and compound 48/80 cause release of serotonin and histamine by different mechanisms and from different cells.

Both thrombin and trypsin release most of the serotonin in platelets within a few minutes. But preincubation with mono-iodoacetic acid or sodium fluoride inhibits both the accompanying glycolysis and serotonin release. The release of serotonin by thrombin has been suggested as one of the mechanisms involved in platelet thrombus formation. However, there are many other ways this can occur.[47] This important subject needs much more penetrating study. The liberation of serotonin by reserpine is slow compared with that by thrombin. Neither thrombin nor reserpine cause concurrent liberation of amino acids (Buckingham and Maynert[54]), showing that increase in membrane permeability of a nonspecific sort does not accompany the serotonin release.

Markwardt and Barthel[215] studied thrombin-induced serotonin release using pure enzyme in suspension of rabbit platelets. The release was very rapid, ending in a few seconds; about 85 to 90 per cent was liberated. The thrombin inhibitor, *hirudin,* completely blocked this action of thrombin. The release was independent of viscous metamorphosis of the platelets. Thus, platelets treated with thrombin in Ca^{++}-free solution released serotonin without morphological change and the metamorphosis occurred only after addition of calcium.

Groth[151] suggested that infusion of thrombin into rabbits released both serotonin and histamine which lowered blood pressure and decreased oxygen turnover in skin. Serotonin also elicited intravascular aggregation of red blood cells. Swank, Fellman and Hissen[326] described *in vitro* and *in vivo* changes in adhesiveness and aggregation of platelets, leukocytes, erythrocytes and slowing or cessation of conjunctival circulation as a result of administration of large doses of serotonin. They suggested that these effects may be a part of the mechanism of hypovolemic shock.

Platelet plugs form, according to Spaet and Zucker,[315] when platelets are exposed to connective tissue or when thrombin releases both serotonin and adenine nucleotides, of which about one-third is the diphosphate. Adenosine diphosphate itself causes clumping of platelets but fails to liberate serotonin, suggesting that the clumping is not influenced by serotonin but rather by the ADP.

Several investigators have published suggestive evidence of the occurrence *in tissue extracts* of a serotonin releasor from both platelets and mast cells of mastocytoma but adequate resolution of the problem has yet to be achieved. Hopefully, a young investigator will isolate and characterize such substances, if such there be.

The myenteric plexus of mice is able to synthesize and bind serotonin when its radioactive precursor 5-hydroxytryptophan is administered, according to Gershon, Drakontides and Ross.[138] Addition of nonradioactive serotonin to *in vitro* preparations is followed by an almost immediate *release* of the stored tritiated serotonin from the region of the myenteric plexus. The authors suggest that the release was the result of stimulation of mucosal sensory nerves, in turn causing release of serotonin from the myenteric plexus. This autorelease of serotonin is inhibited both by the anesthetic lidocaine, and by cold. As a working hypothesis, serotonin is considered by them a neurotransmitter between sensory and motor neurons in the peristaltic reflex pathway.

There are many factors that can deplete or antagonize the serotonin content of brain. For example, it has been shown that depletion is increased with an increase of partial pressure of oxygen. One hundred per cent oxygen depletes both serotonin and norepinephrine in mice brain (Fairman and Heble[113]). It makes one wonder what 100 per cent oxygen does to an astronaut's brain!

The storage and release of serotonin have baffled and intrigued investigators. Recently, Zucker, Hellman and Zumoff[365] presented evidence that platelet-bound serotonin disappears by exchange with tissue serotonin depots rather than by removal of intact platelets from blood as a result of aging or random destruction. It is reasonable to suppose that the central nervous storage compartment has an entirely independent function and mechanism of storage and release from that in the rest of the body, and, since it probably is involved in neural transmission, release from this store will be considered in connection with brain (p. 55). The close proximity of the enterochromaffin cells with the smooth muscle of the gut has suggested that serotonin acts as a part of its propulsion mechanism.

The Possible Singular Importance of Platelets

I was taught that platelets had little importance except when they were lacking, as in thrombocytopenic purpura. They were disparagingly referred to as "blood dust." But more recently they have assumed a vastly increased significance, as indicated by the holding of a full-scale symposium in their honor.[181]

They are clearly involved in formation of white thrombi and the latter are being suspected of playing an important part in the formation of atherosclerotic plaques when they become overgrown with endothelium. On several occasions I have suggested that they were the hemic counterpart of synaptic vesicles—small packets of mobile neurohumors. They do not appear to synthesize serotonin, but absorb it with avidity. Such floating reservoirs could well provide neurohumors for the local control of circulation and aid in hemostasis. A careful comparison of the function of cerebral synaptic vesicles with platelets might disclose many similarities and provide a much more available model of serotonin function and transfer than the synaptic vesicles themselves. For instance, the study by Robinson, Anderson and Green[279] on the uptake of serotonin and histamine by particulate fractions of brain could be repeated using platelets. The half-life of platelet serotonin seems to depend on certain disease states, since it appears to exchange with body stores, according to Zucker, Hellman and Zumoff.[365] This could be measured concurrently in the synaptic vesicles. Then, too, the releasing action of a variety of drugs could be measured on both. Paasonen[232] found that increased plasma concentrations of chlorpromazine liberated nearly all of the platelet serotonin while tetrabenazine or reserpine released only about one-half, indicating a difference of action which might be similar in synaptic vesicles.

Whether there is also a relationship with mast cells remains to be determined.

Breakdown of Serotonin

Oxidative deamination by monoamine oxidase, an enzyme discovered in 1928 by Hare,[164] is the chief mechanism of serotonin degradation in contrast with the catecholamines. Serotonin is first converted to 5-hydroxyindoleacetaldehyde, as originally shown by Udenfriend in 1956, then to 5-hydroxyindoleacetic acid as a result of the action of an aldehyde dehydrogenase. The usual amount excreted in 24 hours in a normal person's urine is from 2 to 10 mg and about 50 to 100 micrograms of serotonin itself.

The major metabolites in the urine are those that result from the action of amine oxidase (McIsaac and Page[204]). More than half of the dose administered is accounted for by 5-hydroxyindoleacetic and 5-hydroxyindoleaceturic acids. Subsequent glycine conjugation occurs, and to a much greater extent in rabbits than in rats. Acetylation also plays a significant role in the metabolism of serotonin, 5 to 25 per cent of the urinary metabolite being in the forms of N-acetyl-5-hydroxytryptamine. Unchanged serotonin accounts for 5 to 9 per cent of the dose. Conjugation with glucuronic acid and ethereal sulfate occurs only to a small extent. The 5-hydroxyindoleacetic acid is excreted almost entirely as a mixture of unchanged acid and its glycine conjugate.

One reason there is some degree of unreliability in using the excretion of 5-hydroxyindoleacetic acid as a test for carcinoid, or for other sources of excess serotonin production, is that it is increased when serotonin-containing foods are consumed such as bananas, tomatoes, avocados, red plums, walnuts and eggplants. Still, as Sjoerdsma has convincingly shown, the excess excretion of this acid remains the most useful and practical method for the diagnosis of carcinoid.

Urinary 5-hydroxyindoleacetic acid has mistakenly been used as a measure of alteration in cerebral or platelet serotonin activity. The amount contributed from these sources is so small that change could hardly be detected, even though the turnover might be rapid.

There is chromatographic evidence for the presence in some urine samples of methylated derivatives of serotonin and, since some of these are psychotomimetic, more than usual interest centers on them. This area, however, needs much more careful and penetrating study than it has so far received.

In 1964, Kveder, Iskrić and Keglević[189] showed that serotonin could be reduced to the corresponding alcohol in rat's liver and found the glucuronide of 5-hydroxytryptophol as a major metabolite in the urine. Subsequently, others have shown its formation by rabbit platelets in the absence of erythrocytes and in the urine of subjects with carcinoid tumors. In normal persons given serotonin, about 2 per cent is excreted as 5-hydroxytryptophol and its conjugates. This major contribution by Kveder has only recently begun to be explored in studies of abnormal serotonin metabolism.

Thus Bartholini, Pletscher and Bruderer[25] found in the incubation medium (Tyrode's solution with reserpine) of isolated rabbit's platelets a neutral metabolite that was partially identified as 5-hydroxytryptophol. It occurs, however, only if no major number of red cells are present, in which case there is exclusive formation of 5-hydroxyindoleacetic acid. While isolated erythrocytes are unable to transform serotonin or 5-hydroxytryptophol into 5-hydroxyindoleacetic acid, they can oxidize added indole acetaldehyde to indoleacetic acid. In contrast, isolated platelets of animals pretreated with reserpine convert the aldehyde primarily to tryptophol. Thus, platelets seem to transform released serotonin into 5-hydroxyindoleacetaldehyde, and the aldehyde is oxidized completely to 5-hydroxyindoleacetic acid in the presence of erythrocytes which presumably contain aldehyde oxidase. Human and rat brain homogenates convert serotonin into 5-hydroxytryptophol and 5-hydroxyindoleacetic acid via 5-hydroxyindoleacetaldehyde according to Eccleston, Moir, Reading and Ritchie.[100] An alcohol dehydrogenase effects the formation of the 5-hydroxytryptophol.

This surely is the barest outline of the problem of the degradation of serotonin. There have been many suggestions and small amounts of evidence that serotonin is converted within the tissues to psychotomimetic substances that could play an important part in mentation. For example, the possible findings of bufotenin in the urine of schizophrenics has been cited as such evidence. But it should be made clear that until much more and better work is available, these suggestions are still only hypotheses worth studying. Methylation of serotonin has opened one vista which is full of promise because so many such substances have strong biological actions. I cannot imagine a more exciting field than the unraveling of the many possible transformations cells can make, starting with serotonin. But its very excitement should warn against too-hasty and melodramatic conclusions.

Action of Serotonin on Invertebrate Carbohydrate Metabolism

One of the most advanced and penetrating investigations on the function of serotonin has been conducted over the years by Tag Mansour.[210, 211]

Monod had shown that certain enzymes, in addition to their catalytic function, act as regulators of metabolic functions. This form of control has been called "allosteric regulation." A metabolite, neither the immediate substrate nor the direct product of the enzymatic action, could activate, or inhibit, its catalytic action by changing its kinetic properties. Mansour gives as a classic example the glycogen phosphorylase system of mammalian muscle studied by Cori. Muscle phosphorylase may be present in an active and inactive form;

the latter becomes active in presence of 3′,5′-AMP. The adenylic nucleotide acts here as an allosteric regulator. A kinase system converts inactive to active phosphorylase and a phosphatase converts the active to the inactive form. Further regulation occurs at this level, since cyclic 3′,5′-AMP activates the phosphorylase kinase. As is well known, Sutherland and Rall showed that epinephrine increases the synthesis of cyclic 3′,5′-AMP. Sutherland suggested that several hormones act by two-messenger systems, the first messenger being the hormone released. At the cell target it releases a second messenger which acts as the intracellular regulator ligand.[325] Cyclic 3′,5′-AMP is the second messenger Mansour has applied with great skill to the thinking on carbohydrate metabolism of the trematode liver fluke.

First, he showed the presence of serotonin and a system which catalyzes its formation from 5-hydroxytryptophan in fluke homogenates. Then, that flukes metabolize carbohydrate at a high rate, predominantly anaerobic. When glucose was available to the intact organism, serotonin caused considerable increase in its uptake. If glucose was unavailable, glycogen utilization was markedly increased by serotonin.[208, 209] These increases were accompanied by a two- to ten-fold increase in lactic acid production. In contrast, epinephrine did not have these stimulant actions. Serotonin also stimulated concurrently the rhythmic movement of the fluke.

Since serotonin increased glycogen breakdown in contrast to epinephrine, Mansour, Sutherland, Rall and Bueding[213] looked for and found that phosphorylase activity was significantly increased after incubation with serotonin which, in turn, led them to consider a possible role of 3′,5′-AMP. Stone and Mansour[323] found that serotonin caused a rapid and specific increase in formation of cyclic 3′,5′-AMP catalyzed by a particulate fraction from the fluke. Epinephrine in this preparation had no such effect.

Since serotonin increases glycolysis by acting on one or more of the glycolytic enzymes, the question arose as to which one. Phosphofructokinase proved to be the rate-limiting enzyme. Serotonin greatly increased the activity of this enzyme. It could even be shown that concentrations which increase glycolysis also increase activity of phosphofructokinase in intact organisms.

Their demonstration that serotonin activates the synthesis of cyclic 3′,5′-AMP suggested that the action of serotonin on phosphofructokinase was mediated through it. Both ATP and Mg++ were found essential for the activation.

Phosphofructokinase, in addition to its property of reversible convertibility from inactive to active enzyme, also exhibits regulatory function based on allosteric inhibition by one of its substrates, ATP. This inhibition of phosphofructokinase by ATP can be reversed by cyclic 3′,5′-AMP. The cyclic nucleotide was shown to increase the concentration of ATP required for the ATP inhibition. Mansour suggests that serotonin could conceivably increase the activity of ATP-inhibited phosphofructokinase, so modulating the activity of the fully activated form of the enzyme (Mansour and Mansour[212]).

Thus, serotonin seems to play much the same part in carbohydrate metabolism in invertebrates that epinephrine plays in higher organisms. In summary, Mansour has shown that serotonin is analogous to epinephrine in increasing formation of cyclic 3′,5′-AMP, phosphorylase activation, stimulation of glycogenolysis and of glycolysis. The rate-limiting phosphofructokinase, in addition to being influenced by serotonin, is also subject to regulation through its allosteric properties. Fluke phosphofructokinase is controlled by two chief mechanisms: (1) conversion of inactive to active form and (2) allosteric regulation of the activated enzyme. Cyclic 3′,5′-AMP importantly controls the enzyme by both mechanisms. It is essential for conversion of inactive to active enzyme and can activate the enzyme when inhibited by ATP through an effect on its allosteric kinetics. Serotonin both activates phosphofructokinase but increases the formation of the cyclic nucleotide. Thus, the effect of serotonin on phosphofructo-kinase is analogous to that of epinephrine on mammalian muscle and liver phosphorylase.

This seems to me to be a remarkably interesting and well-documented investigation showing a clear hormonal effect of serotonin in invertebrate carbohydrate metabolism not shared by epinephrine, which seems to be its counterpart in higher animals. Endoportal administration of serotonin or that endogenously synthesized from 5-hydroxytryptophan produces glycogenolysis, hyperglycemia and stimulation of hepatic phosphorylase activity in isolated perfused rat's liver. This occurs independently of its vasomotor effects on the liver (Levine, Pesch, Klatskin and Giarman[196]). The glycogenolytic action is blocked by the serotonin antagonist 1-methyl-[methyl ergonovine], also called UML-491, or Sansert.

CHAPTER 2

Some Physiological Aspects

Vascular Actions of the Amphibaric Hormone

SEROTONIN HAS WIDESPREAD ACTIONS on the vascular tree of intact animals which result importantly from its effect on peripheral and pulmonary vascular smooth muscle. It has such variable effects on arterial blood pressure that McCubbin and I did the almost unforgivable, created a new word, *amphibaric,* to describe them. We found that serotonin raises blood pressure when neurogenic vascular tone is low and lowers it when the tone is high. Thus, for example,[238, 243] serotonin sharply reduced blood pressure in dogs with neurogenic hypertension and raised it when hypotension was produced by cutting the spinal cord. Inhibition does not depend upon changes in sympathetic vasomotor discharge or ganglion blockade, but upon a more peripheral effect.

The response of the arterial pressure varies widely in different animals. Page[238] found single doses to be pressor with an initial depressor von Bezold reflex in dogs. In contrast, cats, rabbits, rats and chickens' response is chiefly depressor. The response is also dependent upon the mode of administration. Thus, Page and McCubbin[244] observed that intravenous infusions in both dogs and cats elicited a sustained fall while in some hypertensive patients a small, sustained rise occurred. There is also a dose-response dependence.

Apparently, the ability of serotonin to oppose neurogenic

vasoconstriction depends upon adrenergic vasodilatation. The beta-receptors are probably not stimulated directly but are affected by serotonin to increase their sensitivity to neural stimulation. When so stimulated, the resultant decrease in total vascular resistance is caused by dilatation of small arteries and veins (McCubbin, Kaneko and Page[201]). Slow infusion of serotonin usually causes a prolonged fall in pressure. When the beta-adrenergic receptors are blocked with dichloroisoproterenol, the vasodilator action of serotonin in the presence of neurogenic vasoconstriction is eliminated.

Thus, measurement of pressure in vessels of hind limbs perfused by the dog's own circulation showed that stimulation of the lumbar sympathetic trunk causes constriction of both large and small arteries. If serotonin is injected during stimulation, it causes relaxation of the small arteries but further constriction of the large ones; the net effect is decrease in total vascular resistance. In the absence of stimulation, serotonin caused constriction of both large and small arteries and increase in vascular resistance. Using photographic techniques with mesenteric vessels, it was found that small veins respond to stimulation and serotonin as do small arteries.

In perfused dog's leg and rabbit's ear, it is vasoconstrictor with a reflex vasodilator component when the leg maintains nervous connection with the body.

The pressor action of serotonin is greatly augmented by ganglion blockade. The characteristic depressor response in dogs with chronic neurogenic hypertension is a reliable way of identifying hypertension resulting from buffer nerve section.

Serotonin is not the only substance that exhibits such variable amphibaric actions, i.e., vasoconstriction or vasodilation depending upon the particular state of the responding organism. Epinephrine is such a substance but its action is more dose-dependent than serotonin—low concentrations being vasodilator and high, vasoconstrictor. I wonder if the body actually uses such built-in flexibility as a measure furthering functional economy; one substance could either increase or decrease peripheral resistance. It is an intriguing idea worth further study.

As Feldberg and Smith[119] showed, serotonin and trypta-mine, like other monoamines, under some circumstances cause liberation of histamine which may contribute to the long-term vasodilator action. The release was shown with perfused skin flaps, gastrocnemius muscle of cats and rats. Their action is about 100 times less than the polymer compound 48/80.

It had been concluded by Page and McCubbin[244] that the depressor response to serotonin had at least three main contributing mechanisms: (1) release of endogenous histamine, (2) peripheral inhibition of neurogenic vasoconstriction and (3) a dose-response relationship that, in some preparations, determines whether blood pressure will rise or fall.

Serotonin also causes release of acetylcholine from isolated guinea pig ileum (Brownlee and Johnson[53]). The size of the contraction stimulated by serotonin was related to the amount of acetylcholine released. It is becoming increasingly clear that many cardiovascular actions of drugs are influenced by such indirect actions of the agonist. These add immeasurably to the complexity of the mechanisms of their effects.

McCubbin, Green, Salmoiraghi and Page[200] presented clear evidence that serotonin causes a pronounced increase in chemoreceptor impulse traffic in the carotid sinus nerve. Using a perfusion system permitting chemoreceptors to be excluded from the natural circulation, it was found that small doses of serotonin failed to stimulate respiration unless the drug reached them. Chemoreceptor stimulation also contributed to the pressor response elicited by its intravenous injection. Serotonin proved to be an even more powerful chemoreceptor stimulant than lobeline. Comroe and Mortimer[76] devised an ingenious experiment to study the effect of serotonin separately on the aortic and carotid chemoreceptors in dogs. Stimulation of the aortic receptors resulted in tachycardia, while those in the carotid bodies elicited bradycardia, hypotension and marked hyperpnea. It is odd that the cat's carotid body contains relatively large amounts of serotonin (Chiocchio, Biscardi and Tramezzani[74]).

Serotonin is a smooth muscle stimulant in that it causes contraction of isolated arterial strips, denervated nictitating membrane, uterus, intestine, bronchiolar muscle as well as veins and arteries.

Reid,[272] one of the very early workers in the field, studied the effects of serotonin in chloralosed cats showing that the initial fall in blood pressure is associated with an increased resistance within the pulmonary circulation. He also found a direct stimulating action on the adrenal medulla as well as an increased amplitude and rate of heart beat (Langendorff isolated heart).

Unlike most other substances, it has a powerful pulmonary vasoconstrictor action when given as an intravenous infusion into dogs (Rudolph and Paul[284]). Usually the pulmonary vessels have very limited reactivity to drugs. Serotonin has a direct effect as well by increasing cardiac output—both lead to pulmonary hypertension. In dogs, Duteil and Aviado[98] showed the pulmonary hypertensive response is accompanied by an increase in pulmonary blood flow and is partly due to a sympathetic reflex initiated by the pulmonary vasoconstriction of serotonergic origin. In their heart-lung preparations, the hypertensive response to serotonin was largely due to pulmonary vasoconstriction.

There have been many studies of the vascular effects of serotonin in various regions of the body. The most recent, and in some ways the most complete, is that of Vyden, Gold, Bernstein and Corday.[346] They measured blood flow with implanted electromagnetic meters in the internal carotid, left anterior descending coronary, superior mesenteric, renal and main pulmonary arteries of 20 dogs while serotonin solution was infused for 2 hours into the aorta near the coronary ostia.

There were many variations of the hemodynamic effects but mainly when arterial pressure fell, cardiac output and work fell while coronary flow sharply increased. Blood flow also diminished in the mesenteric and renal circulations owing to increased vascular resistance. The serotonin antagonist, methylsergide, reversed all these changes. This is but a sampling of how varied the actions of serotonin are on regional blood flow.

In the forearm and hand of human beings serotonin reduces skin blood flow by constriction of the resistance vessels. Concurrently, venous constriction causes passive dilatation of capillaries resulting in pooling of blood in vessels responsible for skin color and thereby accounting for the observed increased volume of the limb (Roddie, Shepherd and Whelan[280]). Thus, an early flush is followed by cyanosis as the hemoglobin is reduced within the stagnant blood of the capillaries. In the forearm, the large muscle mass complicates interpretation of the result of intra-arterial injection of serotonin. An increase in blood flow within muscle occurs which with increase in dosage changes to reduction (Bock, Dengler, Kuhn and Matthes[39]). Both serotonin and histamine in patients produce effects identical with epinephrine, i.e., arteriolar dilatation and venous constriction (Sharpey-Schafer and Ginsberg[303]) possibly by stimulating beta adrenergic receptors. For those interested in the participation of serotonin in peripheral circulatory control in human beings, I can strongly recommend Whelan's recent book.[354]

A wide range of serotonin concentrations were employed in a convincing study of isolated cat's papillary muscles and canine right heart bypass preparations with both carotid sinus and vagal nerves cut by Buccino, Covell, Sonnenblick and Braunwald. Serotonin increased the contractile state of the ventricular myocardium, augmenting both the rate of tension development and peak isometric tension. In the deafferented canine right-heart-bypass preparation, the positive inotropic action was also shown, as had been found years ago by Erspamer and Ghiretti[110] for molluscan hearts. Stroke volume and aortic flow rates were also increased.

Quite unrelated to its effect on heart, serotonin has interesting central effects on vasomotor activity. Reserpine, serotonin, norepinephrine, 5-hydroxytryptophan and 3,4-dihydroxyphenylalanine were found by McCubbin, Kaneko and Page[201] to have qualitatively the same effects when injected into anesthetized or unanesthetized dog's lateral ventricle. All lowered arterial pressure, usually caused bradycardia despite vagotomy and also inhibited pressor response to carotid artery occlusion. Decreased afferent electric activity of the carotid sinus nerve accompanied the hypotension resulting from intravenous injection of large doses of 5-hydroxytryptophan, or small doses of the amino acid given intraventricularly, indicating that the cardiovascular effects are not due to a direct effect of the amino acid on carotid sinus baroreceptors.

Further work by Kaneko, McCubbin and Page[183] showed that several vasoconstrictor drugs and reserpine administered centrally inhibited the reflex pressor response to carotid artery occlusion. This effect was opposed by central administration of the vasodilator drugs sodium nitroprusside and histamine. Cooling of the cerebrospinal fluid, which presumably caused local vasoconstriction, also caused inhibition of the reflex hypotension and bradycardia. The inhibition resulting from cooling was counteracted by central injection of vasodilator drugs. Warming the cerebrospinal fluid presumably associated with local vasodilation opposed the central inhibitory effects of vasoconstrictor drugs and of reserpine.

In view of the consistently opposite effects of vasoconstrictor and vasodilator drugs and procedures on central sympathetic vasomotor activity, it was tentatively concluded that they depended upon changes in local blood flow. The acute cardiovascular effects of reserpine of central origin are probably dependent upon the same mechanism.

The vasodilating effect of serotonin has been suggested by Horton[172] as being part of the mechanism of reactive hyperemia. He found no increase in plasma kinins in blood collected from dog's hind limb during the stage of hyperemia but rather a seven-fold increase in butanol-extractable substance closely resembling serotonin. It was postulated that serotonin was released from platelets during the period of vascular occlusion to induce the hyperemia which led to increased fibrinolytic activity of blood, so counteracting the tendency for coagulation to occur in the occluded vessels.

Thus, the varied actions on the circulation have led to speculation as to whether serotonin normally, or even abnormally, participates in its regulation. Except in such states as the carcinoid syndrome, its participation is not obvious. But, like other humoral agents, it does not occur in amounts great enough to elicit dramatic responses. In this it behaves as do the catecholamines. It may take its place among other agents in the equilibrated mixture that bathes the vascular smooth muscle. The conception of equilibration among the many controlling facets of the circulation has been further developed as the "mosaic theory" (Page[237]).

Some Effects on Gut

There are those such as Bülbring and Crema[56] who consider that the usual function of serotonin is to regulate the propulsive action of the intestine by stimulation of mechanoreceptors. It facilitates the peristaltic reflex at two sites: (1) mucosal sensory receptors and (2) sensitizing the muscle to the transmitter choline. Recent work by Burks and Long[59] convincingly demonstrates the release of serotonin from gut into venous effluent. Various stimuli such as scratching the serosal surface, intra-arterial administration of acetylcholine and increasing intraluminal pressure were found to increase markedly the serotonin release. Serotonin seems to lower the threshold of excitation of mucosal sensory endings so that a lower pressure in the intestine is required to elicit the peristaltic reflex. Certainly such increased activity occurs in the carcinoid syndrome, adult idiopathic intussusception associated with high intake of bananas and, possibly, in the dumping syndrome.

But serotonin is not essential for propulsion, if the observations and their interpretations are correct (Boullin[46]) that rats fed for 1 month on a tryptophan-free diet are depleted of serotonin, yet peristalsis is unchanged. The response in these so-called depleted animals to intraluminal and serosal application of serotonin did not differ from normal. Also peristalsis was normal *in vitro* in the tryptophan-deficient rats before any serotonin had been given. Although the number of enterochromaffin cells diminishes in such amino-acid deficiency, evidence is lacking that *all* of the serotonin disappeared from the intestine. Possibly the last 10 per cent is responsible for the normal peristalsis, as is true of the vascular action of other neurohumors. Serotonin thus appears to play only an ancillary role as a sensory stimulant for normal peristalsis. This does not mean, however, that in the carcinoid syndrome the increased gut motility is not due to serotonin.

From the observation that isolated rat's stomach strips are contracted by tryptamine and the contraction is potentiated about 20 times by amine oxidase inhibitors while those elicited by serotonin are not. Handschumacher and Vane[162] wrote that tryptamine, which is much more soluble in lipid than serotonin, enters the cell during development of contraction. That which enters is rapidly metabolized to 5-hydroxyindoleacetic acid; the breakdown is abolished by amine oxidase inhibitors. Serotonin which is relatively insoluble in lipid enters the cell during contraction only in very small quantities, hence is unaffected by amine oxidase inhibitors. In their work, radioactive tryptamine and serotonin were used to measure the entrance of these substances into smooth muscle during the muscle's contraction. Changes in pH of the bathing fluid substantially alters the relative activities of the two amines, probably due to shifts in their lipid solubility, leading to changes in cell penetration. The concentrations of serotonin at the receptors was found independent of cell penetration, or the activity of amine oxidase inside the cell and was relatively independent of changes in pH as well. The lack of potentiation of serotonin contractions by amine oxidase inhibitors was explained by Vane[344] on this basis.

Effect of Serotonin on Temperature Control

One unusual function for serotonin was suggested by Feldberg and Myers[118] on the basis of the finding that the rectal temperature of anesthetized cats was sharply elevated by injecting serotonin into the cerebral ventricles. Oddly, catecholamines lowered it. This reciprocal action appeared to be mediated by the hypothalamus. Dogs and rabbits behaved similarly.

The fluid in the third ventricle evidently contains serotonin because perfusion with artificial cerebrospinal fluid washes some of it out. Further, if its destruction is reduced by amine oxidase inhibitors, the output in the effluent increases. The increase is associated with shivering and rise in temperature (El Hawary, Feldberg and Lotti[103]). On the other hand, if the inhibitor tranylcypramine is injected intraperitoneally during the fall in temperature produced by pentobarbital anesthesia, the serotonin output also increases, shivering occurs and the fall in temperature is reversed.

If the precursor of serotonin, 5-hydroxytryptophan, is perfused through the cat's third ventricle, the effluent shows an increased output of serotonin which is proportional to the concentration of the amino acid. All of the above experiments were done with anesthetized animals and the question arises as to what occurs when the animals are conscious. In cats, the effects of serotonin and catecholamines were the same, i.e., serotonin raised the temperature and catecholamines lowered it. El Hawary and Feldberg[102] found that the injection of serotonin into unanesthetized cat's cerebral ventricles elicited a biphasic rise in temperature, tachypnea, wiping and scratching movements, mewing and long-lasting sleep. Feldberg explained the biphasic rise as a result of two opposing effects of serotonin, the one an increased serotonin effect which would raise temperature and the other a central depressant effect which would lower it.

Cooper, Cranston and Honour[77] also found biphasic effects of both norepinephrine and serotonin when injected into the lateral ventricles or anterior hypothalamus of conscious rabbits. Whenever either hormone failed to alter body temperature, an injection of bacterial or leukocyte pyrogen into the same site caused fever, showing the mechanism of temperature response was intact.

Injection of serotonin into the 3rd cerebral ventricle in two goats at normal body temperature and during pyrogen-induced fever caused peripheral vasodilation, polypnea and a marked fall in brain, right heart and rectal temperature while small amounts of catecholamines failed to alter the rectal temperature.[12] All of these results leave doubt as to the place of the more usual notion of hormonal factors in temperature regulation.

Further, when serotonin was administered intraventricularly to dogs both temperature-sensitive and temperature-insensitive single units in the pre-optic-septal area reduced their discharge rate.[88] These findings do not support the proposed antagonistic role of serotonin and epinephrine in maintenance of body temperature. On the contrary, recent work on the differential effect of heat and cold on the activity of central monoamine neurons by Corrodi, Fuxe and Hökfelt[81] indirectly indicate participation of these neurons in thermoregulation.

It is impossible on the basis of present evidence to know whether or not this mechanism is a physiological one. Temperature control, like blood pressure control, is certainly regulated by highly complex mechanisms. To separate out one and contrast it with another is usually to overemphasize the separateness of each. A reasonable assumption would be that the action of serotonin on hypothalamic centers, along with catecholamines may be *part* of a temperature-regulating mechanism but is far from being the whole.

CHAPTER 3

The Brain and Its Serotonin

WHEN CEREBRAL METABOLISM or "brain chemistry" was being established as a field worthy of study, serotonin played an extraordinary role. It will come as a surprise to younger readers that even as late as 1937 many scientists were dubious as to whether "neurochemistry" was indeed a discipline[235]; some even questioned at this late date whether transmission of a nerve impulse consumed oxygen! If I had to select a single effect resulting from discovery of serotonin, I would unhesitatingly suggest its influence in shaping investigators' ideas on cerebral activity. These have already developed so fast that even though large numbers of serotonergic nerves have been traced, their functions remains to be investigated.

Distribution

Shortly after its discovery, Twarog and I,[336] in examining its distribution in the body, were surprised that relatively large amounts of serotonin were contained in brain. Amin, Crawford and Gaddum[4] confirmed this and made a careful study of its cerebral regional distribution.

The great Swedish school of investigators discovered so much about the occurrence of monoamines in neural tissue, I can confidently leave the story to them, being content to remind the reader of such names as Hillarp, Carlsson, Falck, Hökfelt, Corrodi, Bertler, Fuxe, Andén and Dahlström.

Fortunately, Hillarp, Fuxe and Dahlström have recently published a most competent review[170] and, for those primarily interested in the brain, I strongly recommend a magnificent summary by Fuxe, Hökfelt and Ungerstedt.[130]

In 1962, Carlsson, Falck and Hillarp[67] introduced the fluorimetric method for catecholamine determinations in tissue which Falck further improved by using formaldehyde as a condensing agent to bring out the fluorescence. Serotonin reacts to form 3,4 dihydronorharman derivatives which have an intense yellow fluorescence. Falck[114] mapped the occurrence of serotonin in brain with this method. It is notably concentrated in hypothalamus, pineal region and in some neurons.

High concentrations of serotonin are found in the hypothalamus while those in the neopallium and cerebellum are low. Using assays, Paasonen, MacLean and Giarman[233] found in dogs the relatively high serotonin values of the cortex limited to limbic structures. Central serotonergic neurons contain low concentrations in the cell bodies and high in the terminal portion. It is mainly localized in the bead-like varicosities or vesicles of the nerve endings where it is stored in granules (De Robertis and Bennett[93]).

The serotonergic neuron cell bodies are found mainly in the raphe nuclei of the lower brain stem and some of them are also found surrounding the pyramidal tract and in the medioventral part of the caudal tegmentum. Almost none occur in the diencephalon, telencephalon or spinal cord. Electron microscopic studies of the cells in the nucleus raphe dorsalis show well-developed granular reticulum and prominent Golgi apparatus around the nucleus. Granular vesicles are seen mainly in the serotonin-rich zone surrounding the nucleus, probably representing a storage site. The varicosities of the terminals seem to be presynaptic structures.

The largest number of serotonergic nerve terminals has been found in the lumbar enlargement and the sacral portion of the cord. Large numbers are found in the autonomic sacral nucleus, the sympathetic lateral column and in some visceral efferent nuclei of the pons and medulla. The lower brain stem is rich in them. Terminals are also diffusely scattered in most parts of the reticular formation.

The fact that serotonergic nerve terminals are found in both sympathetic and parasympathetic nuclei shows that they are not alone concerned with regulation of parasympathetic functions.

Another problem of interest to investigators is that various strains of mice have clear differences in the cerebral content of serotonin as well as regional differences (Sudak and Maas[324]). The days are over when all that seemed necessary was to mince the whole brain from an animal and measure the total serotonin content.

If levels of 5-hydroxyindoleacetic acid reflect the cerebral metabolites of the parent serotonin, then the demonstration by Ashcroft, Eccleston, Crawford, Sharman, MacDougall, Stanton and Binns[18] might have significance. They found decreased amounts in spinal fluid obtained by lumbar puncture from depressed patients as compared with those with other neurologic diseases, and suggest a defect in synthesis, or release, of serotonin by the brains of such persons. Low values were found in the acute phase of depression by Denker, Malm, Roos and Werdinius,[91] with a slow rise to normal values on recovery. The concentration was also low during the manic period but somewhat higher than during depression. The cerebrospinal fluid content of 5-hydroxyindoleacetic acid more closely related to mental changes than did homovanillic acid. Carrying this work further, Johannson and Roos[179] compared its content in normal persons and patients with Parkinson's syndrome. In most of the latter it was also decreased.

Spinal cord section removes the influence of action potentials on nerve terminals lying caudal but not cranial to the lesion. Andén, Fuxe and Hökfelt[8, 9] found this removal of nerve impulse flow greatly to affect the depletion of serotonin and norepinephrine stores after inhibition of the enzymes tyrosine and tryptophan hydroxylase. In contrast, depletion by reserpine was much less dependent upon nerve impulse flow. Thus, they distinguish two types of depleting drugs, those dependent and those independent of nerve impulses. The inhibitors of biosynthesis belong to the former, i.e., tyrosine hydroxylase inhibitor (alpha-methyl-p-tyrosine), tryptophan hydroxylase inhibitors (alpha-propyldopacetamide), decarboxylase inhibitors (Ro 4-4602) and the dopamine-beta-oxidase inhibitor (diethyldithiocarbamate). The effect on amine levels of drugs that inhibit uptake and storage in the amine granular (reserpine and tetrabenazine) are relatively independent of impulse flow. This means that the amine movements from granules to cytoplasm are not influenced by action potentials. Amines are degraded by monoamine oxidase in cytoplasm when the uptake-storage is blocked. But if the uptake mechanism is intact, as after inhibition of synthesis, the amines released from granules are taken up almost quantitatively. When serotonin or norepinephrine is released from neural vesicles by the nerve impulse, part of the amines is lost. This loss is normally compensated for by synthesis. Thus, they conclude that when synthesis is inhibited, the rate of amine disappearance indicates the magnitude of the nerve impulse flow. Reduced to molecular levels, this could provide data of great physiological importance.

They also found that nerve impulses stimulate synthesis much as they do in the adrenal medulla, at least for catecholamines. When action potentials were absent, serotonin and norepinephrine synthesis seemed reduced by about two-thirds, a figure of the same order of magnitude as that observed for loss of 5-hydroxyindoleacetic acid in rabbits' spinal cord caudal to a transection (Andén, Magnusson, Roos and Werdinius[11]). The regulation of serotonin synthesis can occur in absence of granules since it was noted in reserpine-treated animals.

Changes in Serotonin Content

The amount of serotonin in brain is probably chiefly dependent upon the amount of tryptophan in the diet, although sharply reducing it does not eliminate it from animal's brain. Tryptophan enters the brain by active transport and other amino acids may compete for the same mechanism. This is one of the key problems and one of the potential major approaches to cerebral metabolism. The turnover of serotonin in brain is fast in contrast with that in peripheral tissues.

There have been many conflicting reports on whether serotonin can pass the blood-brain barrier (summary by Bulat and Supek[55]). Ionized and lipid-insoluble substances, in general, pass through capillary walls poorly and serotonin is both ionized and low in lipid solubility. Still, most evidence shows that very small amounts when injected intravenously, or intraperitoneally, penetrate the brain and are metabolized within a matter of minutes. As compared with the amount taken up by liver and lungs, it is small; nonetheless, it may have physiological actions.

Besides daily rhythmic changes in certain areas of the brain, there are also those due in some animals to activity and hibernation. Uuspää[341] showed that during winter sleep the serotonin content of the hedgehog brain was always higher, especially in the hemispheres, than in midsummer. Electrical activity is greatly reduced during hibernation as is the norepinephrine content. These two probable transmitters appear to function in different systems of the brain.

Inhibitors of monoamine oxidase such as nialamide cause a rise in both serotonin and norepinephrine content of mouse brain, whereas dopamine is scarcely affected. A characteristic syndrome ensues in which the animal becomes restless, exhibits enhanced spontaneous motility and head movements (Carlsson and Corrodi[65]). By using different inhibitors of the synthesis of these amines it could be shown by Corrodi[80] that only substances that block the synthesis of serotonin inhibit the development of the nialamide syndrome. Both major classes of antidepressive drugs exhibit important effects on serotonin-mediated actions.

Carlsson has also shown an increase in spinal cord serotonin after administration of nialamide. After transection of the cord (T2), no serotonin or norepinephrine was found below, which supports the view that several bulbospinal descending serotonergic and adrenergic neuron systems are present in the cord. More specific destruction of areas of the brain may produce changes in either norepinephrine or serotonin without necessarily affecting both, suggesting again different distribution of serotonin from norepinephrine-producing fibers.

Extensive studies of the effects of destructive lesions on the serotonin content of brain have been made by Heller and Moore.[166, 167] They conclude that destruction of areas demonstrated to lower brain levels involve neural elements either within or directly related to the neurons of the medial forebrain bundle. Section of the tract itself greatly reduces the levels throughout the telencephalon. Lesions more caudally in the midbrain tegmentum may, depending on their location, alter either serotonin, norepinephrine, or both. It is not known why the medial forebrain bundle is critical for the maintenance of cerebral monoamines, although its importance as the primary source of hypothalamic afferent and efferent connections is known. But this is a complicated problem expertly discussed in Heller and Moore's short review.[168]

Effects of Serotonin on Neural Function

First let me strongly recommend an excellent review by Costa on the general role of serotonin in neurobiology[82] and a slightly later one by Costa, Gessa, Hirsch, Kuntzman and Brodie.[84]

There is some evidence, reviewed by Trendelenburg[333] that intra-arterial injection of serotonin into the blood supply of the cat's superior cervical ganglion causes stimulation of the ganglion, and is abolished by nicotine or cocaine but unaffected by hexamethonium or atropine. He also found that serotonin potentiated the response of the nictitating membrane to submaximal preganglionic stimulation but not to supramaximal stimulation. Trendelenburg views these results as supporting the notion of the presence of tryptamine receptors in the superior cervical ganglion possibly similar to those said to exist in the nerve tissue of guinea pig ileum. This interesting concept needs much further exploration.

Many single interneurons in cat's spinal cord are responsive to the electrophoretic administration of serotonin (Weight and Salmoiraghi[350]).

Neurons of the olfactory bulb reduce their spontaneous discharge rates when serotonin is administered microelectrophoretically, suggesting that serotonin and possibly other endogenous amines participate in the functions of olfactory inhibitory synaptic pathways. Bloom, Costa and Salmoiraghi[38] confirmed this reduction of spontaneous discharge rate by administering acetylcholine, norepinephrine or serotonin to individual nerve cells in unanesthetized rabbits. The amines are not dependent for their effect upon intact stores of serotonin, norepinephrine or dopamine.

The excitatory effect of microelectrophoretic administration of serotonin on the spontaneous firing of sympathetic preganglionic neurons in the fourth thoracic spinal cord segment of anesthetized cats was studied by de Groat and Ryall.[150] Many of these cells were excited, a few were depressed also by norepinephrine while acetylcholine was inactive. This does not suggest that serotonin is an inhibitory transmitter acting on the sympathetic neurons. To establish this, it must be shown that the action of the transmitter liberated by selective activation of serotonergic nerve fibers is identical with that of serotonin.

Jequier[177] measured the effect of serotonin on the transmission through the superior sympathetic ganglion of rats, finding it was slightly depressed. The precursor, 5-hydroxy-tryptophan, behaved similarly. This *in vitro* experiment did not suggest any powerful or highly specific effect of serotonin.

One of the strange effects of the intracarotid injection of serotonin is that on cerebral cortical evoked optic response (Koella, Smythies, Levy and Czicman[186]). A receptor area for this effect is in the carotid sinus, and stimulation induced a change in activity in the neuronal net of the reticular formation, leading to change in activity of the ascending, unspecific, diffusely projecting systems. Change in intrasinus pressure alone altered the degree of activity measured in the EEG. Spontaneous fluctuations in activity of autonomic centers and of the unspecific modulating structures in the brain stem were intimately coupled. Application of serotonin exclusively to cat's perfused isolated carotid sinus area prepared for recording cortical visual response showed the lowest and highest doses caused inhibition while the intermediate doses elicited facilitation. This is one of several examples of the potent but variable influences of serotonin on neuronal activity. Does such an experiment adumbrate those in which normally occurring amounts will be shown to affect the EEG?

Serotonin as a Transmitter

Recently, Pax and Sanborn[250] conducted an extended study of the possibility that serotonin is an endogenous inhibitory transmitter of the Limulus heart but were unable to be certain of this. In crustacean hearts there is little doubt that serotonin is a strong cardiotropic substance (Maynard and Welsh[220]). These diametrically opposed actions are quite in keeping with the nature of serotonin.

It is known that brain slices incubated in suitable media maintain their bioelectrical and biochemical activity for several hours. Electrical stimulation of isolated spinal cord releases endogenous serotonin. Schanberg[291] found that serotonin accumulates, especially in the nerve terminals, when such slices are incubated in a suitable medium. Serotonin released by electrical stimulation has been shown to occur by Chase, Breese and Kopin.[73] They injected tritiated serotonin into anesthetized rat's cisterna magna and prepared the brain slices after 15–30 minutes or they prepared them from unanesthetized rats and incubated them with H^3-serotonin. The slices were held between electrodes and, by superfusion, the efflux of radioactivity was measured. Demonstration of stimulus-induced release depended upon use of relatively low concentrations of serotonin and was dependent upon the amplitude of stimulation. Marked regional differences were noted, the slices from cerebellum being low relative to hypothalamus and striatum. The amount of stimulation-induced release seemed to follow the endogenous content of each tissue or a high density of serotonergic terminals. A high release did not occur with either H^3-water or C^{14}-urea. Addition of lysergic acid diethylamide partially inhibited the release. These results are similar to those obtained with norepinephrine.

Chase, Breese, Carpenter, Schanberg and Kopin[72] have effectively summarized data derived from study of the cardio-accelerator system of the mollusc *Aplysia* to show that serotonin has neurotransmitter function, i.e., it is present in nervous tissue, releasable by nerve stimulation, local administration is accompanied by the same cardiotonic effect as nerve stimulation and is blocked by concentration of antagonists that interrupt the actions of serotonin. Also, Gerschenfeld and Stefani[137] have presented impressive evidence of transmitter function in neurons of snails having serotonin receptors. Stimulation of the nerve afferents to the central ganglia during 3 hours increased ten times the resting "spontaneous" release of serotonin. The serotonin receptors on the membranes of these neurons are highly sensitive.

Evidence for the transmitter function of serotonin has come from the study of molluscan neurons by Gerschenfeld and Stefani.[136] The specific effect of serotonin, the membrane conductance of ganglia of Argentine land-snail and the presence of specific serotonin receptors fill some of the criteria required to consider a substance as a synaptic transmitter. They also showed blockade of serotonin receptors by LSD derivatives in extrasynaptic receptors of snail neurons, and suggested the reasonable hypothesis that serotonin is the natural excitatory transmitter for these neurons.

Somewhat similar conclusions have been drawn by Aiello and Guideri[3] from their study of the relationship between serotonin and nerve stimulation on ciliary activity. The rate of ciliary beating in the gill of the muscle *Mytilus edulis* was greatly increased by electrical stimulation of the branchial nerve. If nerve activity causes release of serotonin, depletion of it by reserpine or blockade by bromolysergic acid diethylamide should diminish the cilio-excitatory effect. This occurred: the rate of ciliary beating was, however, unrelated to the total concentration of serotonin in the gills. Rather, it seemed dependent upon the concentration of free serotonin, which in turn may have been determined by branchial nerve activity. Perhaps somewhat similar phenomena are encountered in the bioluminescence of the animal, Meganyetiphases. Serotonin added to sea water makes it glow spontaneously and respond much more actively to flash stimuli. These effects are blocked by the anti-serotonin 2'- (3'dimethylaminopropylthio) cinnamalide, according to Doyle.[96]

Andén, Dahlström, Fuxe and Larsson[7] showed increased efflux of endogenous serotonin from isolated spinal cord resulting from electrical stimulation. The levels of serotonin in brain respond to certain pharmacological agents as well. Barchas and Freedman[24] extended this to the effects of severe stress. They showed that in rats swimming to exhaustion the stress led to an increase in brain serotonin and concurrent decrease in norepinephrine.

Heller and Moore[167] have demonstrated the interesting selective nature of the effect of central nervous system lesions on serotonin and norepinephrine content in rat's brain. They provide strong evidence of the occurrence of specific amine-producing neurons dependent for their amount upon the integrity of the neurons in the central nervous system.

Gertner, Paasonen and Giarman[142] found serotonin in the perfusate of functioning cat's superior cervical ganglion when iproniazid was added to the perfusing fluid. The ganglion also produced much more when the precursor, 5-hydroxy-tryptophan, was also added. But the appearance of serotonin was not dependent upon neural stimulation. We are left with the feeling that it must have a transmitter function, but clear proof is lacking.

One of the more convincing experiments suggesting the importance of serotonin as a transmitter is that of Stark, Boyd and Fuller,[320] in which electrodes were implanted in the area of the medial mamillary nucleus of the posterior hypothalamus of dogs. The dogs were trained to press a lever for electrical self-stimulation, and the thresholds were measured. Drugs such as alpha-methyl dopa which lower cerebral norepinephrine, dopamine and serotonin resulted in marked depression of self-stimulation response. This inhibiting effect correlated best with serotonin levels. If serotonin was elevated and norepinephrine unchanged, threshold was also lowered. The serotonin antagonist bromolysergic acid diethylamide (BOL) lowered the threshold although high doses raised it. A monoamine oxidase inhibitor which elevated brain serotonin lowered the threshold. In this self-reward system serotonin seems to play an important part.

In rat's brain the largest collection of neuronal perikarya containing serotonin is located in the raphe area of midbrain. According to Aghajanian, Rosencrans and Sheard,[2] electrical stimulation for 30 minutes of this area produces an increase in 5-hydroxyindoleacetic acid and a decrease of serotonin in the forebrain. This indicates that serotonin can be released through specific neural pathways, namely, those axons projecting into the forebrain from serotonin-containing neurons in the midbrain raphe. Stimulation of the lateral midbrain did not produce change in concentration of either indole. Almost certainly serotonin is concerned in the mechanisms of cerebral transmission.

Some years ago, Marrazzi and Hart[217] demonstrated that serotonin transiently blocked cerebral transmission when injected into a cerebral artery. This may have been due in part to the action on cerebral blood vessels because norepinephrine behaved similarly. Thus, Kaneko, McCubbin and Page[183] showed that vasoconstrictor and vasodilator drugs have consistently opposite effects on central vasomotor activity and concluded that the vasoconstrictor aided in central inhibition. There are probably other more direct inhibitory or augmenting effects which remain to be demonstrated.

Marrazzi and Hart were convinced that serotonin played a highly important part in neurohumoral synaptic inhibition, overshadowing epinephrine and norepinephrine by virtue of its greater potency. When given by arterial injection into a common carotid artery the serotonin was believed to penetrate the blood-brain barrier to be able to inhibit the ipsilateral cortical synapses, as indicated by reduction in cortically recorded action potentials. The high potency of serotonin appeared to be characteristically cerebral, since the synaptic inhibition they had recorded in the ciliary ganglion required about 75 times the dose. Marrazzi has shown that many chemical psychotogens are synaptic inhibitors and suggests that serotonin or similar substances are likely candidates for the role of endogenous psychotogens acting by distorting synaptic equilibria (Gluckman, Hart and Marrazzi[145]).

According to Bertler, serotonin is equally distributed between sympathetic nerve fibers and the parenchymal cells of rat's pineal gland. If pineal decarboxylase is inhibited, most of it quickly disappears, suggesting a rapid turnover of serotonin in pinealocytes. The pineal cells almost certainly secrete serotonin. An intact sympathetic innervation does not seem to be necessary to control the turnover rate.

Circumstantial evidence of the transmitter function of

serotonin is provided by the occurrence of enzymes in synaptic structures that destroy or synthesize it. For example, McCaman, McCaman, Hunt and Smith[199] found high concentrations of monoamine oxidase and of 5-hydroxytryptophan decarboxylase in rabbit's synaptic tissue.

Lastly, recent work by Jouvet[182] supports the view that the serotonin-containing cells in the nuclei of raphe induce sleep. He postulated that in cyclic fashion the serotonin of the raphe system and the norepinephrine of the *locus ceruleus* apply brakes to the reticular activating system responsible for wakefulness, so controlling sleep. This concept could lead to important physiological and clinical understanding.

While the evidence is fragmentary, still it adds up to the probability that the serotonin in the serotonergic nerve has an inhibitory transmitter function, which is especially prominent in lower animals and an excitatory one as well, being more accentuated in higher animals. The high concentration of serotonin in the pineal and hypothalamic areas suggests still other cyclic functions. What it comes to is that the function and metabolism of the cerebral indolealkylamines are only dimly perceived but even though dim their vast importance can hardly be mistaken.

Evidence gathered by Andén, Carlsson and Hillarp has left little doubt in their minds that serotonin is a transmitter. They cite (1) the similar distribution to that of norepinephrine in nonadrenergic neurons, (2) electrical stimulation of the axon causes release and increased synthesis of serotonin, (3) the origin of serotonergic neurons in the lower brain stem and termination in various parts of the brain and spinal cord innervating, for example, spinal sympathetic centers in the intermedio-lateral nucleus and (4) the fundamentally similar actions of reserpine on catecholamines and serotonin. Blockade of storage mechanism is clear evidence in favor of this hypothesis. It should be recalled that only a few years ago the majority of investigators emphatically took the opposite view.

Some Mechanisms Probably Concerned in Transmission

Carlsson[63] distinguishes three kinds of release of monoamines at nerve endings:

(A) Release by the nerve impulse which seems to act on
a small transmitter pool within the storage granules.

(B) Spontaneous leakage through the axon membrane.

(C) Spontaneous loss from the granules into the axoplasm.
Other important processes that influence release are their
formation and breakdown. These mechanisms are balanced
by uptake mechanisms working oppositely.

(D) Pumping through the axon membrane back into the
axoplasm.

(E) Incorporation into storage granules.

Clearly the net transfer will depend upon an equilibrium
among these varied forces. It can be shown that uptake
mechanisms (D) and (E) are disturbed by selective blocking
— (D) by antidepressive agents of the imipramine type and
(E) by reserpine, tetrabenazine and Segontin. Besides, there
are compounds which serve as substrates for the uptake
mechanism capable of competing with endogenous amines
with these and binding sites as well. There is evidence that
neurons are able to discriminate to some extent between
precursor amino acids by selective amino acid uptake. The
structural specificity of the uptake mechanisms is not very
high. There is still a further group of compounds which
block granule storage as well as the membrane pump; tyramine and guanethidine are examples. A detailed examination
of these problems has been made by Fuxe, Hökfelt and
Ungerstedt[130] and is readily available.

The difficulty with using inhibitors of the synthesizing
enzymes of serotonin is that it is almost impossible to block
them wholly so that all function is extinguished. The amount
of stored transmitter needed to carry out many of the characteristic actions of serotonin is extraordinarily small.

The granule mechanism plays a key role in both uptake

and release. Amine uptake can be blocked by two classes of agents: (1) a lipid-soluble group that penetrates the blood-brain barrier and does not depend upon a membrane pump, e.g., reserpine, and (2) a polar group unable to penetrate the barrier that requires the membrane pump for penetration of the neuronal cell membrane. The first group is the more important in relation to serotonin.

Since there is much less evidence directly concerned with serotonin, an analogy with the function of norepinephrine can be drawn. Thus Folkow, Häggendal and Lisander[124] found that even when no sympathetic fiber discharge was present there was slight norepinephrine release from nerve fiber varicosities after membrane pump blockade. This seems to reflect a random release of quantal "packets" of the transmitter unmasked after blockade of the pump. During stimulation at normal ranges of 6 imp/sec of all vasoconstrictor fibers to calf muscles, the norepinephrine release for stimulus per 100 g of muscle was about 0.15 ng, a minute amount compared to the total store; perhaps about 3 per cent of the norepinephrine content of one adrenergic granule released for each stimulus from the individual nerve varicosity. This corresponds to approximately 400 norepinephrine molecules in which each granule appears to contain about 15,000. Most evidence suggests that the major part of the norepinephrine content of adrenergic fibers forms a storage pool, while only a minor fraction is immediately available for release. This available norepinephrine is rapidly exhausted if the fibers are driven at above-physiological frequencies. Further, if the re-uptake mechanism is blocked, exhaustion of this transmitter fraction is more rapid. Normally, the active norepinephrine re-uptake combined with synthesis easily keeps the available store largely constant.

Consistent with earlier investigations, it was shown that by far the most important route for local elimination of transmitter at the vasoconstrictor nerve endings is the re-uptake mechanism accounting in the calf muscle for 70 to 80 per cent of the released amount, at least during rest. The major portion of the remainder escapes into the blood stream. Enzymatic destruction at the neuroeffector junction seems negligible. If the re-uptake mechanism fails, transmitter elimination by means of diffusion is such a slow process that rapid reflex adjustments for the efficient control of the cardiovascular system is impossible.

Serotonin and Circadian Rhythm

Quay and Halevy[264] in 1962 showed in rats a circadian rhythm for pineal serotonin dependent for its timing upon periods of lightness and darkness as well as some modification by the estrus cycle. The rhythm is an intrinsic one, since injection of serotonin does not alter it. Subsequently, Quay has published a large series of penetrating studies on this phenomenon in various animals.[261, 262, 263]

The very high serotonin level of pineal gland is distributed equally between parenchymal cells and sympathetic nerve fibers arising in the superior cervical ganglia. The circadian rhythm of serotonin described by Quay[260] involves both of these storage sites. Serotonin is synthesized by the rat's pinealocytes according to Falck, Owman and Rosengren.[116] They studied the changes in pineal serotonin concentration after inhibition of synthesis and breakdown with various drugs during daylight to achieve a relative steady state. A rapid turnover of serotonin was found in the pinealocytes independent of the sympathetic innervation even when daylight allowed for a large buildup of serotonin. The turnover rate was considerably higher than in the intrapineal nerves. Curiously, treatment with monoamine oxidase inhibitor caused no significant increase in pineal serotonin while eliciting a three-fold rise in neuronal serotonin in brain.

Owman[231] points out that serotonin is probably secreted by the pineal cells, since that present in the intrapineal nerves is taken up from the pinealocytes, with displacement of norepinephrine. An equilibrium between the nervous and parenchymal pools of serotonin may explain the estimated 30 per cent decrease of serotonin in pineal nerves concurrently with loss of parenchymal secretion upon treatment with decarboxylase inhibitors.

A circadian rhythm has also been found for pineal tyrosine hydroxylase, the rate-limiting enzyme in catecholamine synthesis (McGeer and McGeer[203]). Quay recently found the same for melatonin. Many of the intermediary mechanisms concerning these rhythms have been elucidated by Axelrod and his associates. Wurtman, Axelrod and Fischer[359] recently found that exposure to light reduces the ability of rat pineal gland to synthesize melatonin. When the sympathetic nerves to the gland are cut, light no longer has this effect, which is also true for serotonin (Snyder, Zweig and Axelrod[313]). This important relationship of the sympathetic innervation of the pineal gland to diurnal rhythm has been effectively reviewed by Axelrod.[19] The response was independent of the gonads or the pituitary gland. This is important evidence suggesting a concurrent role of catecholamines and indolealkylamines in regulatory function.

Lerner, Case, Takahashi, Lee and Mori[195] were probably the first to call attention to the high indole content of the mammalian pineal region when they extracted N-acetyl-5-methoxy-tryptamine and called it "melatonin." The serotonin content is also exceptionally high, as Giarman and Day[143] found in 1959. Melatonin originates by biosynthesis from serotonin through O-methylation of N-acetylserotonin (Axelrod and Weissbach[21]).

Quay found that the level of serotonin fluctuated sharply during the course of 24 hours and was correlated with periods of lightness and darkness. Similar circadian rhythm occurred in both male and female rats but in the latter there were differences associated with the day of the estrus cycle.

There has accumulated a wealth of interesting information about the effects of drugs and sympathetic denervation on the pineal content of the various components of the serotonin-melatonin complex.

When female rats are exposed to continuous illumination, there is a decrease in activity of the pineal, hydroxy-O-methyl transferase, which synthesizes melatonin. This effect of light is blocked by central lesions bilaterally transecting the medial forebrain bundle in the lateral hypothalamus (Wurtman, Axelrod, Chu, Heller and Moore[358]). Sympathetic denervation of rat's pineal gland causes many changes in enzymatic activity concerned with serotonin and norepinephrine in the gland (Snyder, Axelrod, Wurtman and Fisher[311]). This neural effect in altering the activity of an enzyme may apply to other tissues following sympathetic denervation to explain such phenomena as the increase in myocardial glycogen after denervating the heart. The circadian rhythm of serum serotonin in healthy men and male patients with mental retardation has been studied by Halberg, Anderson, Ertel and Berendes.[158]

The importance of studying such changes as occur in circadian rhythm, I suspect, lies chiefly in the fact that the *regulation* of a body constituent is measured. Too long we have thought only in terms of a static configuration which takes little account of the mechanisms the body uses to regulate its constituents. Another example of this kind of study concerns the demonstration that the lateral hypothalamic area exerts control over sodium intake; the chemical mechanisms are not yet known.

Melatonin

Serotonin seems to be concerned with skin pigmentation both in having a direct effect on melanophores and in being the mother substance of melatonin contained primarily in the pineal region. Melatonin was discovered in 1959 by a remarkable dermatologist named Lerner, who was associated with Case and Heinzelman. Serotonin is converted *in vivo* to the N-acetyl derivative, then to 5-methoxy-N-acetyl tryptamine, showing its close metabolic relationship to serotonin. It is the most potent skin-lightening agent known in amphibians, but it is not operative on similar mechanisms in mammals.

Julius Axelrod and Richard Wurtman, in their usual elegant fashion, showed that the pineal gland contains all the enzymes and substrates necessary for the formation of melatonin in the following two steps:

serotonin *acetyl CoA*—N-acetyl serotonin *S-adenosylmethionine*— melatonin.

The subject has recently been reviewed by them.[22]

As so often happens, a tumor is identified that synthesizes biogenic amines, and from Wurtman and Kammer's recent finding[360] melatonin is no exception. They found an ectopic pinealoma containing high levels of the melatonin-forming enzyme, hydroxyindole-O-methyl transferase, an enzyme usually located solely within the pineal gland. It is worth remembering that more often the tumor with its signs and symptoms is found well before the chemical mechanisms causing the latter are identified. It is almost as though nature had prepared a clue so that those of us who spend our lives in the game of Treasure Hunt will have something to guide us.

CHAPTER 4

Psychotropic Drugs, Mental Disease and Serotonin

Reserpine and Serotonin-Kinetics

IN 1955, Pletscher, Shore and Brodie[255] made the remarkably interesting observation that reserpine caused a sharp decrease in concentration of serotonin in many tissues by blocking storage. Brodie, Pletscher and Shore suggested a causal relationship between the depletion, but not the actual content, of cerebral serotonin to the tranquilizing effect of reserpine. This was shortly followed by the observation of Carlsson and Hillarp[69] and Holzbauer and Vogt[171] that the catecholamines were similarly affected. These observations set off a blizzard of papers which, although now somewhat abating, still continues. In a short space I cannot do justice to this important debate.

In essence, the chief problem is whether specific depletion of brain monoamines causes the sedation and other clinical signs resulting from reserpine. Brodie and Shore[52] proposed that serotonin and norepinephrine modulate opposing functional systems described in the brain by Hess. The *ergotrophic* portion affected by norepinephrine is concerned with arousal, increasing sympathetic activity and enhancing skeletal muscle tone and responsiveness to external stimuli. The *trophotropic* system integrates behavioral patterns that are recuperative in nature and hence are predominant in sleep and hibernation. Increasing its activity results in sleep, increased central parasympathetic output and lowered responsiveness to external stimuli. Serotonin may modulate this system (Brodie and Reid[51]).

There have been many studies attempting selectively to deplete either serotonin or norepinephrine; however, it has proved difficult to affect one but not the other and, further, it is not clear how *much* depletion is necessary to elicit physical signs. Brodie suggests that there is a direct association between recovery of the storage mechanism which is normally responsible for the uptake and storage of serotonin and dissipation of the signs. Applied steady-state kinetics show that serotonin, norepinephrine and dopamine stores, though present in constant amount in brain, are in continual flux, with synthesis balancing efflux. This integration is controlled by "neurochemical transducers" that translate electrical impulses into the discharge of precise amounts of neurohormones to the receptor. Brodie considers them the "primary units of behavior," since the organism responds to environmental change only because these units control the quantity of free neurohormone at nerve endings.

The central effect of reserpine was found to be a function of the initial rate of release as expressed by the proportion of serotonin stores that disappear per minute (Brodie, Comer, Costa and Dlabac[49]) rather than the final degree of depletion. These results do not prove that the central action of reserpine is caused by change in serotonin but show two associations requiring exploration: (1) the close relationship between the initial rate of serotonin release and the intensity of the reserpine-action and (2) the association between the recovery mechanism in brain that takes up serotonin and recovery of animals from sedation. Brodie's kinetic analysis of serotonin release suggests that the *primary* action of reserpine is to inhibit the carrier process at nerve endings. He is convinced that reserpine sedation is associated with changes in cerebral serotonin rather than with catecholamines. This is supported by Spector, Sjoerdsma and Udenfriend's finding[317] that alpha-methyl-tyrosine which blocks catecholamine synthesis does not elicit sedation until catecholamines are reduced 90 per cent or more, while reserpine produces it in doses that deplete stores of serotonin and norepinephrine only about 55 per cent.

As I will discuss (p. 85), Koe and Weissman discovered that p-chlorophenylalanine lowers cerebral serotonin specifically and prevents the rise after administration of monoamine oxidase inhibitors. The drug inhibits the rate-limiting tryptophan hydroxylase. But pretreatment with it does not prevent reserpine sedation! As long as amine uptake by the granules and the rest of the transmission machinery function normally, the amount of stored transmitter needed for nerve function is amazingly small, suggesting that the effect of p-chlorophenylalanine does not provide as critical an experiment as it was first thought. Brodie and Reid[51] counter this with the observation that after administration of maximal doses of p-chlorophenylalanine, the synthesis of C^{14}-serotonin from C^{14}-tryptophan injected directly into the hypothalamus is about 30 per cent of normal. It may be that the reduction of serotonin in the brain is insufficient to block the central action of reserpine by analogy with the decline to 10 per cent in norepinephrine necessary to produce chlorpromazine-like signs when d-methyltyrosine is given.

Brodie's studies seem to indicate that the tranquilizing effects of reserpine and chlorpromazine involve different neural pathways. Chlorpromazine appears to inhibit the central ergotrophic action of catecholamine. In contrast, reserpine causes trophotropic stimulation temporarily associated with impairment of the mechanism responsible for the uptake of serotonin in cerebral neurons.

Only time and much investigation will tell whether this is a correct explanation of the central actions of reserpine but, regardless of the outcome, much important information on the dynamics of brain metabolism is being brought to light.

The view that serotonin has little to do with the central action of reserpine has been championed especially by Carlsson. Much of his evidence is concerned with dopamine and norepinephrine and, therefore, will not be discussed. Perhaps one of his most telling arguments is that metatyrosine partially protects the stores of norepinephrine in brain against the action of reserpine, while those of serotonin are left essentially unprotected. The gross reserpine syndrome was largely prevented by protecting the cerebral catecholamine stores and thus supports his evidence from experiments with monoamine precursors. Dopamine depletion may well turn out to be important for development of the syndrome (Carlsson and Lindqvist[71]).

Carlsson[62] is convinced that a causal relationship between reserpine and a monoamine has been established only in adrenergic neurons; doses of reserpine which deplete norepinephrine also block adrenergic transmission. The degree of norepinphrine depletion and blockade of transmission *are* closely correlated but only very small amounts of transmitter are essential for function; a store of transmitter is not necessary. Blockade of transmission by reserpine cannot be wholly explained by reduced tissue norepinephrine levels. Carlsson believes the additional action necessary is blockade of the uptake mechanism in the storage granules because this mechanism seems even more closely correlated with reduced transmission.

Storage granules have a dual function: (1) to act as transmitter stores and (2) to make newly formed transmitter available for release of neural activity. Only the latter function seems essential under normal conditions and it is directly dependent on a specific, reserpine-sensitive uptake mechanism. But, if this mechanism is blocked by reserpine, transmission can still take place at the expense of the store.

Psychotropic Drugs and Serotonin

The literature on this problem is vast and would suffer from being touched lightly. We cannot do better than to use Pletscher's orientating schema to expose the problem. He outlines the following five types of action of these drugs:

1. Decrease of storage capacity for monoamines—rauwolfia alkaloids and benzoquinolizine derivatives.

2. Decrease of synthesis—alpha propyldopacetamide, alphamethyl dopa, p-chlorophenylalanine.

3. Inhibition of monoamine oxidase—iproniazid, nialamide, harmaline. The excitation induced by monoamine oxidase inhibitors appears to be largely due to accumulation of serotonin, as shown by experiments with specific inhibitors of synthesis.

4. Interference with monoamine penetration—chlorpromazine. However, this effect is probably secondary to hypothermia.

5. Increase of sensitivity of central nervous receptors— imipramine and amitriptyline. This "sensitization" is apparent only; it is due to blockade of the "amine pump" at the level of the cell membrane of monoaminergic neurons, leading to an increased serotonin level at receptor sites. The sensitivity of the receptors themselves is not increased but, if anything, decreased.

There are many drugs that affect these various aspects of both serotonin and catecholamine metabolism. Let us consider just a few examples.

Antidepressive Agents Such as Imipramine

Much recent evidence indicates that both serotonin and catecholamine-storing neurons in the central nervous system take up and concentrate amines by a specific reserpine-resistant mechanism, which can be blocked by antidepressive agents of the imipramine type.

According to Bertie and Shore,[32] there appear to be two amine-concentrating mechanisms in *adrenergic* neurons. One functions within the neuronal membrane to facilitate uptake from extracellular fluid while the other operates intraneuronally on the amine storage granules. The latter is blocked specifically by reserpine, tetrabenazine and low concentrations of guanethidine; the membrane mechanism by cocaine, bretylium, ouabain and imipramine and, being an energy-requiring system, is considered to be an *amine pump*. Cocaine, desipramine, chlorpromazine and bretylium act as competitive inhibitors of the pump while ouabain is noncompetitive.

Since Sigg's discovery[301] that *imipramine* potentiates the action of norepinephrine and sympathetic nerve stimulation in the peripheral nervous system, the view has been favored that a similar augmenting effect on central norepinephrine might account for its antidepressive action. The peripheral potentiation is probably due to blockade of an amine-concentrating mechanism in the cell membranes of adrenergic neurons. While derivatives of imipramine proved active inhibitors of this mechanism in the central norepinephrine neurons, imipramine itself was found comparatively weak by Carlsson, Fuxe and Ungerstedt[68] despite its good antidepressive action. They have recently found in the central serotonergic neuron a reserpine-resistant uptake-concentrating mechanism which is blocked by imipramine.

To demonstrate this, intraventricular injections of serotonin were made into the lateral ventricles of rats pretreated intraperitoneally with reserpine and nialamide. Imipramine was given intraperitoneally 15 minutes before the serotonin. This resulted in marked blockade of the reserpine-resistant concentrating mechanism for serotonin in the serotonergic cell bodies, nonterminal axons and terminals lying close to the ventricles. This, as well as other evidence they have gathered, suggests the importance of this action for the antidepressive action of imipramine of blocking the reserpine-resistant concentrating mechanisms.

There seem to be different structural requirements for blockade between the noradrenergic and serotonergic neurons. Protriptyline and desipramine are much more active inhibitors of the membrane pump of central noradrenergic neuron than imipramine and amitriptiline (Carlsson[60]). But for the serotonergic neurons the reverse holds true. This led to the tentative conclusion that stimulation of the noradrenergic neurons causes behavioral "activation," i.e., release of the inhibition often seen in depressed patients, whereas stimulation of the serotonergic neurons causes elevation of mood. This may be related to the observation that in depressed patients the level of 5-hydroxyindoleacetic acid in the cerebrospinal fluid is frequently low.

Different antidepressive drugs acting on central adrenergic and serotonergic neurons have been compared and found to be highly variable in their effectiveness. Protriptyline and desipramine were especially potent on the adrenergic and imipramine, amitriptyline and nortriptyline on the serotonergic. Comparing these effects with clinical experience or antidepressive activity, the impression was gained that the adrenergic neurons cause activation and the serotonergic, mood elevation.

Serotonin and Mental Disease

Any suggestion concerning the cause of mental disease inevitably receives attention no matter how meager its justification. Such is true for serotonin in this relationship. The facts are that serotonin can be produced, stored and destroyed in the brain. On isolated uterus, its contractile action is antagonized by LSD but whether the psychotomimetic action of LSD is affected by serotonin in intact brain is unknown. Some indolealkylamines are hallucinogens and produce behavioral disturbances. There is some evidence that tryptophan metabolism may be abnormal in certain mental patients.

There has been much fancy, the chief bit probably that conjured by the great pharmacologist, Gaddum, who made the much-quoted and totally unsupported epigram, "It is possible that the serotonin in our brains plays an essential part in keeping us sane." This was so much nonsense and Gaddum knew it! But it still might be true. The best case for the participation of serotonin in mental disease was made by Woolley in his book, *The Biochemical Bases of Psychoses or the Serotonin Hypothesis about Mental Diseases*. The brilliant discoveries by A. Hofmann at the Sandoz Laboratories in Basel of both LSD and psilocybin have contributed greatly to the basic interest if not understanding of this aspect of cerebral metabolism.

The idea of involvement of precursor amino acids in the mechanisms of mental disease has been tested in a number of ways. One was to administer large amounts while the patient was receiving monoamine oxidase inhibitor. Pollin, Cardon and Kety[256] found methionine and tryptophan changed the behavior of schizophrenic patients. There appears to be a relationship between behavioral worsening and rise in urinary tryptamine. Recently, clinical evidence suggests that tryptophan (5-7 g/day) was as effective in treating severe unremitting depression as electroconvulsive therapy. Addition of monoamine-oxidase inhibitor somewhat improved on tryptophan alone (Coppen, Shaw, Herzberg and Maggs[78]).

Since N,N-dimethyltryptamine has psychotomimetic actions and serotonin is its precursor, Bumpus and Page[57] sought and found evidence for the presence of serotonin, N-methylserotonin and bufotenine in pooled human urine. Subsequently, there has been much conflicting evidence concerned with the occurrence of such methylated serotonins in body fluids of both normal persons and schizophrenics. The most recent, and probably the most carefully controlled, study is that by Tanimukai, Ginther, Spaide, Buenos and Himwich,[328] which clearly demonstrated the presence of bufotenine in the urine of schizophrenic patients. Identification was made by paper, thin layer and gas-liquid chromatography. Exogenous sources of preformed catechol- and indole-amines were excluded from the diet although it was not possible to exclude their formation within the gut. Administration of tranylcypromine, a monoaminoxidase inhibitor, increased the excretion of bufotenine. It was noted that worsening of the behavioral symptoms started about 2 weeks after bufotenine increased in the urine. Fischer and Spatz[122] have also developed a simple paper chromatographic method for determination of bufotenine.

Bufotenine had been discovered in toad skin long before serotonin was known, but its physiological importance was overlooked. Erspamer, Vitalli, Roseghini and Cei[111] have with great profit and skill re-examined this rich source of indolealkylamines. They showed the Arizona desert toad skin contains bufotenine as the most abundant representative of the 5-hydroxyindolealkylamines while O-methyl-bufotenine represents the 5-methoxyindolealkylamines. Oddly, the skin also contains three sulfur-containing indolealkylamines as well as all the known metabolites from the oxidative deamination of these two series of compounds.

Much has been rightly made of the association of phenylalanine excess in the blood with the occurrence of mental disease. Woolley has insisted that experiments carried out in mice with induced phenylketonuria show the cause of this mental defect is deficiency of serotonin imposed early in infancy. Associated with the presence of serotonin deficiency was a loss of mental alertness which disappeared when the deficiency was prevented, even though the subjects continued to have experimental phenylketonuria.

Recent evidence has supported the view that mental state and behavior are more closely associated with the norepinephrine content of brain than of its serotonin content,

but many competent investigators do not agree. The introduction of effective chemical antagonists is beginning to
throw some light on this vexing problem. Alpha-methyl-tyrosine inhibits the enzymes synthesizing norepinephrine, and
its clinical use shows concurrent interference with con-
ditioned avoidance behavior and possibly arousal. If the serotonin antagonist p-chlorophenylalanine is given in large doses
to animals, sleep is suppressed, which is correctable by administering 5-hydroxytryptophan. Engelman, Lovenberg and
Sjoerdsma[104] gave this highly effective serotonin antagonist
to patients with carcinoid, finding that its chief effect was
relief of gastrointestinal distress. It had little effect on the
flushing. The patients reported, when receiving large doses
(3 to 4 grams), a variety of symptoms—listlessness, depression,
insomnia, anxiety, confusion, delusions and hallucinations.
It should be noted that the blockade of serotonin synthesis
was not complete since the change in urinary 5-hydroxyin-
doleacetic acid indicated a reduction of 72 to 88 per cent.
Further, it is not unlikely that the antagonist itself may have
pharmacological properties not attributable to its antagonism
to serotonin. Clearly, the last word has not been said on this
highly complicated problem of the relationship of monoamines to behavior and mentation. As so often turns out to
be true, it may be one important facet.

The proposal that schizophrenia itself arises from abnormalities of cerebral serotonin metabolism was greeted with
some degree of awe. The sort of thinking as reflected in *The
Atlantic Monthly* was pretty heady stuff and reflects the
"newer" approach to scientific communication. Unfortunate-
ly, the experiments on which these important suppositions
spring are not good enough. To advance significantly the
field of psychobiology must probably take solid and un-
spectacular small steps before the giant strides; typical old
man's advice!

The careful studies by Costa and Aprison[83] on the serotonin content of human brain showed no difference whether

it was from psychotic or normal subjects. The measurement of the total amount of a substance does not necessarily give a clue to its disturbed metabolism. One of the first lessons to be learned from isotopic labeling was how erroneous such reasoning could be. Even though such measurements have repeatedly been made, the amount of blood serotonin or urinary 5-hydroxyindoleacetic acid is not likely to reflect intracerebral metabolism of serotonin.

A hint, and it is only that, of possible disturbance of indolealkylamine metabolism comes from studies of cerebrospinal fluid (Ashcroft, Eccleston, Crawford, Sharman, MacDougall, Stanton and Binns[18]). They assume that levels of 5-hydroxyindoleacetic acid reflect the cerebral metabolism of serotonin. The levels were found to vary depending upon the point at which the fluid was sampled. At the same point, they were lower (10.3 ng/ml) in depressed patients than in some other neurological diseases (19.1 ng/ml).

There is also evidence that mentally defective children have elevated blood serotonin levels. Thus, Schain and Freedman[290] noted that increased levels are present only in some of the more severely defective ones; consistently abnormal elevations occurred only in those with autism; the levels were not correlated with the clinical signs. It is not known whether this disturbance of serotonin homeostasis has any significant relationship to the behavioral disorders of these children.

I subscribe to the views (1) that serotonin is a neural transmitter, (2) that abnormality of indolealkylamine metabolism may be shown to result in mental disturbance and (3) that cerebral metabolism of this class of substances is a most promising field for investigation. The road ahead will be long, dangerous and more than usually subject to the distractions of unsupported, exaggerated claims. More capable workers and fewer expositors of brain chemistry are what is needed. Clearly, this field has fallen heir to the current disease of science—too many journals, too many meetings and too little worth talking about!

Antagonists of Serotonin

Gyermek[154, 155] divides the antagonists into (1) ergot alkaloids (natural and synthetic), lysergic acid diethylamide (LSD), 2-bromo-LSD, methysergide (Deseril or Sansert), 1-methyl-D-lysergic acid butanolamide (UML-491), (2) indole compound, (3) antihistaminic agents, (4) phenothiazines, (5) antidepressants, (6) adrenolytic agents, (7) atropine, (8) procaine, (9) morphine and (10) arylguanidines.

It is a curious fact, as I have already pointed out, that part of the interest created by the discovery of serotonin in the brain resulted from the observation of Gaddum that LSD effectively blocked the action of serotonin on *intestinal strips.* From this, the possibly erroneous suggestion was made that the hallucinogenic action of LSD was due alone to blocking the cerebral function of serotonin. Later it was found BOL, 2-bromo-lysergic acid diethylamide, although also blocking the action of serotonin on intestine, had only a limited mental effect.

Even though the line of thought based on LSD antagonism of serotonin has not been established, a large body of evidence implicates indolealkylamines in behavioral disturbances. But Isbell, Winer and Logan[175] showed that high-potency serotonin antagonism *as measured on isolated smooth muscle* is not correlated with high potency as a psychotomimetic.

Freedman and Giarman[129] have given much thought and study to the mechanisms of cerebral actions of amines. In general, they found that pharmacological studies provide only an "initial statement" of the effects of a drug or behavior. Thus, shifts in the level or status of cerebral amines correlate with the *onset* of a psychophysiological state; but the succession of autonomic and behavioral events have yet to be linked with a specific program of neurochemical events. Freedman[126] has shown that LSD increases brain serotonin and decreases norepinephrine. Following the administration of 200 μg LSD intravenously, its concentration in brain rapidly diminishes (half-life calculated at 20 minutes). As the drug leaves the particulate fraction, serotonin levels begin to rise. The onset of behavioral effects occurs between 3 and 5 minutes and recovery at 25 to 35 minutes. The behavioral change correlates with *changing* levels of drug and amines. Bromo-LSD, which has little behavioral effect, does not produce these changes while yohimbine, which in man elicits specific "anxiety," also produces change in serotonin concentration. Those interested in these aspects of serotonin must read the many contributions of these two investigators.

Diaz, Ngai and Costa[94] also found significant decreases in cerebral norepinephrine and dopamine following LSD. Bromolysergic acid failed to affect either serotonin or 5-hydroxyindoleacetic acid levels in brain. They concluded that LSD probably decreases the turnover rate of serotonin.

The observation that LSD powerfully antagonized serotonin stimulated the Sandoz Laboratories in Basle to utilize more fully their prior interests in ergot alkaloids. Cerletti soon found that *most* lysergic acid derivatives had some inhibitory action. The butanolamide, methylated in position 1, given the name, *Deseril*, was the most effective antiserotonin found. It proved both a superior antagonist to LSD on the isolated uterus and was reasonably specific. The structural relationships among these compounds is shown in Figure 3.

In animals, LSD elicits similar effects to those from drugs which cause increased serotonin levels in the central nervous system (see review by Mantegazzini[214]). It seems possible that LSD interferes with serotonergic nerve transmission, especially since it had been shown (Freedman[128]) that it increases the serotonin content especially of the particulate fraction of rat's brain within 10 minutes of its administration. LSD *in vivo* or *in vitro* did not change the net synthesis of serotonin from 5-hydroxytryptophan. For these reasons Andén, Corrodi, Fuxe and Hökfelt[6] studied the effect of LSD upon the activity of the central monoamine-containing neurons utilizing monoamine synthesis inhibitors. Amine depletion

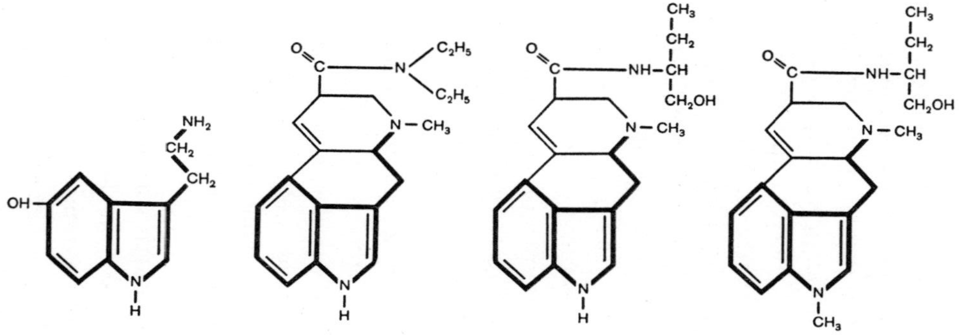

Fig. 3.—Structural formulae of serotonin and three lysergic acid derivatives.

5-hydroxytryptamine
Serotonin

D-lysergic acid
diethylamide
LSD 25

D-lysergic acid
butanolamide

1-methyl-D-lysergic acid
butanolamide
Deseril

obtained with such inhibitors is highly dependent upon nerve impulse flow.

LSD but not 2-bromo-LSD decreased greatly the rate of amine depletion following inhibition of synthesis in these serotonergic neurons by alpha-propyldopacetamide, which indicates that it decreases the neuron impulse flow. This follows, because it had been demonstrated by Andén, Fuxe and Hökfelt[8] that the serotonergic terminals caudal to a spinal cord section, which lack nerve impulses, are not depleted following inhibition of synthesis. The functional studies on spinal reflexes demonstrated LSD and 5-hydroxytryptophan to have similar actions. Since the central action of LSD appeared also in reserpine-alpha-propyldopacetamide pretreated rats, these effects of LSD may be partly the result of direct stimulation of the serotonin receptors of the postsynaptic neurons and not to a release of neuronal serotonin. They also suggest that such direct stimulation evokes a negative feedback on the presynaptic serotonergic neurons, thus resulting in decreased neuronal activity, as indicated by the chemical studies. These results, then, are taken to mean that serotonin receptor stimulation may be responsible for some pharmacological effects of LSD and possibly the hallucinogenic ones as well. This hypothesis is supported by the fact that nonhallucinogenic lysergic acid derivatives do not produce either the chemical or functional changes noted after LSD.

Thus, a brilliant hypothesis sprung from the earlier study of Carlsson and Lindqvist[70] on the effect of chlorpromazine on formation of 3-methoxytyramine and normetanephrine in mouse brain, in which they suggested that the accumulation of these catecholamine metabolites was enhanced due to inhibition of monoamine oxidase inhibition. Compensatory activation of monoaminergic neurons after blockade of the receptors was suggested as the cause. The degree of receptor activation by the transmitter itself or a mimicking analog,

appears to control the impulse flow of the presynaptic serotonergic neuron via a negative feedback.

Chlorpromazine is a less specific antagonist and is actually
an antihallucinogen. It has also proved useful in treatment
of the signs and symptoms of carcinoid tumors. Bartlet[26] has
evidence that it does not impair storage of serotonin but
rather reduces the basal metabolism which, in turn, is a
result of the chlorpromazine-induced hypothermia.

p-Chloramphetamine derivatives *selectively* reduce the
serotonin content of rat's brain, according to Pletscher, Burkard. Bruderer and Gey.[254] There is little concurrent reduction of catecholamines. Because p-chloromethamphetamine,
unlike reserpine, decreases cerebral serotonin after inhibition
of monoamine oxidase by pargyline, Pletscher[253] concluded
that a different mechanism caused the decrease—one involv-
ing pathways other than monoamine oxidase-aldehyde dehydrogenase.

The p-acetylphenethylamines, in particular p-acetyl desoxyephedrine, effectively lower brain serotonin also (Dubnick,
Rucki and Phillips[97]) but in fairly high dosages (5-120 mg/
kg). The central nervous stimulation of the drug was prevented by reserpine pretreatment, but pretreatment with
p-acetyl desoxyephedrine did not antagonize the lowering of
serotonin caused by the reserpine.

Serotonin antagonists such as cyproheptadine (1-methyl-
4-5-dibenzo- (a,e)cycloheptatrienylidenepiperidine hydrochlo-
ride) may also be strongly antihistaminic. Stone, Wenger,
Ludden, Stavorski and Ross[322] have shown its ability to block
the depressor effects of histamine as well as the vasopressor
actions of serotonin in ganglion-blocked anesthetized dogs.
It also stops the spasmogenic effect of serotonin on isolated
rat uterus, the edema produced in rats' feet by local injection
of serotonin and the similarly induced egg white-edema. Its
antihistamine action equaled that of chlorpheniramine and
its antiserotonin effect that of LSD. This drug is said to be

effective in urticaria (Bailey[23]), hay fever (Miller and Fishman[221]), tension headache (Bondi, Siegler, Brown, Gershenfeld and Nodine[42]) and dumping syndrome (Johnson, Sloop and Jesseph[180]).

Antagonists have proved their worth in treatment of varied diseases. The potential participation of serotonin in inflammatory and autoimmune phenomena make their study unusually promising. Methylsergide, which results from methylation of the indole nitrogen of lysergic acid (see Fig. 3) is widely used and is a potent serotonin antagonist to combat "vascular headaches," as well as rheumatoid arthritis and Raynaud's phenomenon. Success has been variable. Methysergide may be associated with the occurrence of retroperitoneal fibrosis and, therefore, must be used with caution.

Woolley[356] has synthesized a variety of serotonin analogues which have antimetabolite actions. BAS or 1-benzyl-2-methyl-5-methoxytryptamine is probably the best known. The most potent one without itself having serotonin-like action is 1-benzyl-2-methyl-5-tryptamine oxyacethydrazide. An even more systematic study has been made by Offermier and Ariëns.[228]

One of the most recent groups of compounds exhibiting strong antiserotonin activity was synthesized by Krapcho and Turk.[187, 188] The 2'- (3'dimethylaminopropylthio) cinnamanilide and related compounds such as those resulting when aminoalkyl groups were added on to the amide nitrogen, a meta-methoxy group introduced into the benzene ring or a benzyl group on the amide nitrogen (Dombro and Woolley[95]) and were found to be both potent and relatively specific.

Cremata and Koe[86] have recently shown that p-chlorophenylalanine reduces the level of serotonin in both cerebral and other tissues, without concurrently lowering that of the catecholamines. It produced in human beings fatigue, dizziness, nausea, uneasiness and fullness in the head.

Koe and Weissman[185] showed that in mice, rats and dogs,

p-chlorophenylalanine specifically depleted serotonin as well as 5-hydroxyindoleacetic acid in brain, yet elicited almost no behavioral changes. This is one of the reasons for questioning whether the effects of reserpine are due to serotonin depletion. In rats, p-chlorophenylalanine reduced the normal increase in 5-hydroxy-3-indolyl compounds resulting from L-tryptophan loading, prevented the increase in brain serotonin which accompanies inhibition of monoamine oxidase by pargyline and blocked the increase in 5-hydroxyindoleacetic acid observed after reserpine treatment. It also inhibited hepatic tryptophan hydroxylase *in vitro*. They suggested that this specific depletor inhibits the biosynthesis of serotonin by blocking tryptophan hydroxylation. Blockade of uptake of tryptophan might also contribute to its effect on decreasing serotonin synthesis. While p-chlorophenyl pyruvic acid exerted essentially the same effects as p-chlorophenylalanine, there are reasons for being skeptical as to whether it is the active metabolite.

Isolated rabbit's aorta contracts when norepinephrine, histamine or serotonin is applied. The chemical similarity of these three aryl-alkyl-amines suggested they might share a common receptor. Wurzel[361] tested this hypothesis by blocking each separately—serotonin with N-dimethylamine-N-benzyl-m-metoxycinnamamide, histamine with mepyramine and norepinephrine with dibenzyline. Thus, three receptors were identified instead of a common one.

CHAPTER 5

States in Which Serotonin
May Be Involved

1. Active Rheumatoid Arthritis and Rheumatic Fever

SCHERBEL AND HARRISON[292, 293] in 1958 first described the abnormal reaction of the hands of patients with active rheumatic arthritis to either intradermal or periarticular injection of serotonin. Contrasting with histamine, epinephrine, norepinephrine and acetylcholine, serotonin caused pain, swelling, erythema and severe cyanosis, all of which were quickly blocked by the serotonin antagonist 2-bromo-d-lysergic acid diethylamide. Halpern, Kuhn, Shaftel, Samuels, Shaftel, Selman and Birch[160] have suggested that patients with Raynaud's syndrome have a similar response to serotonin.

The phenomenon is an impressive one, at least in the patients I have seen, but its significance is unclear. Equally uncertain is the meaning of a report of Haddox and Saslaw[157] that the urine of 48 patients with rheumatic fever and only 1 of 33 nonrheumatic subjects contained 4-methoxytryptamine. Further, it is greatly increased by tryptophan loading. The metabolism of tryptophan seems to take some remarkable twists under varied disease states!

The collagen in nodules of rheumatoid arthritics is characterized by having a shrinkage temperature lower than normal. Highton and Garrett[169] have shown that only serotonin and substances with somewhat similar structure reduced this in *normal* human collagen. Histamine and norepinephrine had no effect, while 5-hydroxytryptophan and 5-hydroxyindoleacetic acid raised it. They suggest that serotonin importantly affects collagen both in rheumatoid arthritis and in the carcinoid syndrome.

2. Anaphylactoid Reactions

For many years, histamine was believed to be the major humoral agent involved in the mechanisms of anaphylaxis. Certainly many of the signs are accounted for by this substance. Recently, this has been questioned as the result of an odd variety of experiments in animals and as evidence also of the action of serotonin in such diseases as carcinoid. The substances more generally concerned in response to tissue injury may have relevance.

When antigen was added to blood from sensitized animal, serotonin and concurrently histamine were released from platelets, as first shown by Humphrey and Jaques.[173] During anaphylaxis, marked and prolonged diminution of circulatory platelets occur. Then it was shown that if antigen were injected into sensitized rabbits, free serotonin and histamine appeared in the plasma (Waalkes, Weissbach, Bozicevich and Udenfriend[347]). Maximum levels were reached in 1 minute and declined to control values within 2 to 3 minutes.

Selye[296, 298] has summarized his thinking about the anaphylactoid edema he first described in 1937. He observed that intraperitoneal injection of egg white into rats caused extensive hyperemia and edema. The reactions always are closely related to the function of mast cells while giving rise to a great variety of structurally distinct lesions. In rats it provides a good method for screening antihistamines, antiserotonins and related antiallergic and antiphlogistic drugs.

Serotonin itself also produces a type of edema in rats not unlike that elicited by histamine (Rowley and Benditt[283]) but about two hundred times as much histamine is required. West[353] concluded that the egg-white reaction was mediated through release of serotonin, probably by increasing capillary permeability. According to the animal species, it might be expected that serotonin and histamine participate in such tissue reactions to varying degrees. Thus, the pulmonary results of anaphylaxis in different species are correlated with the relative amounts of tissue serotonin and histamine (Weissbach, Waalkes and Udenfriend[351]). Since mouse lung contains predominantly serotonin, and that of guinea pig mainly histamine, antihistamine drugs block the response in guinea pigs and LSD part of the hypersensitivity in mice. Human lungs resemble guinea pig in amine content. According to Sjoerdsma,[306] the release of serotonin comes from platelets, not tissues, and could gain access to organs such as the lungs by entrapment of platelets. This would also account for the sharp reduction of their numbers during hypersensitivity reactions and a rise in pulmonary serotonin, at least in rabbits. This is not wholly accepted as an explanation.

Inhalation of a mist of a solution of serotonin by guinea pigs produces dyspnea and sneezing which are abolished by giving the serotonin antagonist methysergide (Wulfsohn and Politzer[357]). But asthmatic *patients* showed no intradermal hypersensitivity to serotonin and during acute attacks there was no increase in urinary excretion of 5-hydroxyindoleacetic acid.

Egg white-sensitized and normal mouse arteries are much more susceptible to serotonin than to histamine. Further, the anaphylactic contraction of sensitized uterus is prevented by reserpine. Fink[121] suggested that the Schultz-Dale reaction and even the systemic anaphylactic reaction in mice are due to serotonin. BOL blocks the reactions. From studies on the relationship of serotonin and the enterochromaffin cells to anaphylactic shock in mice, Gershon and Ross[139] propose that serotonin depletion is responsible for the protection against shock given by alpha-methyl dopa and reserpine. They point out that the chromogenic material of enterochromaffin cells is depleted by anaphylactic shock.

But Sanyal and West[287] found no evidence that serotonin or histamine is involved in producing the signs of anaphylactic shock *in rats* because shock occurs even when the skin and intestine are depleted of both amines. Specific antagonists of both amines similarly fail to modify the severity of the shock. In guinea pigs and rabbits, both serotonin and histamine are involved while in dogs, histamine alone.

There is some evidence (Antopol and Chryssanthou[14]) that serotonin plays a role in the Shwartzman phenomenon. Both antiserotonin and antibradykinin compounds inhibit it and the combination of the two is most effective. The inhibition, however, is limited to the congestion, hemorrhage and edema; leukocytic infiltration and thrombosis still occur.

The finding of serotonin in mast cells by Benditt, Wong, Arase and Roeper,[29] and the fact that they are known to contain histamine and heparin as well, has suggested their importance in response to *tissue injury.* Again, there are large species differences, mouse mast cells containing serotonin and some others not (Sjoerdsma, Waalkes and Weissbach[308]). Since those in man do not, patients with *urticaria pigmentosa,* in whom there are accumulations of mast cells under the skin, exhibit elevated tissue and urinary levels of histamine but normal 5-hydroxyindoles. The same was true in a patient with splenic mastocytoma.

This must make it clear that these phenomena are much too complicated to be touched on as lightly as has been done. There seems to be a high degree of species specificity, and surely serotonin is only one of many facets of these varied tissue responses.

3. Serotonin in Oligemic and Endotoxin Shock

The occurrence of platelet thrombi and the decrease in platelets seen during hemorrhagic or oligemic shock led

Page[236] to suggest the possible participation of serotonin in the complex mechanisms of both myocardial infarction and shock. Comroe, van Lingen, Stroud and Roncorini[75] made a similar proposal for its participation in the mechanism of pulmonary embolism. All of these areas still are largely unexplored.

Acute hypovolemic "shock," as measured by the degree of hypotension, was elicited in heparinized, anesthetized dogs by Swank, Hissen and Fellman.[327] Marked aggregation of red cells occurred. Using C^{14} serotonin, an increase in circulating radioactivity up to 600 per cent was found during the hypotension, representing serotonin or its metabolites. UML-491, an inhibitor of serotonin as well as red cell aggregation in vitro, was shown to reduce the aggregation in vivo during hemorrhage.

Rosenberg, Lillehei, Longerbeam and Zimmerman[281] believe their results from studies in dogs show that endotoxin shock is always accompanied by hyperserotonemia and so differ from hemorrhagic shock. In contrast, occlusion of the superior mesenteric artery in dogs causes a rise in serum norepinephrine and hematocrit but not in serotonin.

One of the persistent questions in circulatory dynamics is whether serotonin plays a regulatory role. Normally, the amount of free serotonin in plasma is small; most of it is bound to platelets. Whether either source is available for control of tissue perfusion has yet to be established. However, the vascular changes occurring in carcinoid show that in certain pathological states it may importantly affect the circulation, it being one of a constellation of vasoactive substances involved in this syndrome.

4. Teratogenic Effect

Subcutaneous injection of single large doses of serotonin into pregnant mice produces a large number of fetal abnormalities (Poulson, Robson and Sullivan;[257] Reddy, Adams and Baird[270]). Recently it has also been shown to be strongly teratogenic in rats (Marley, Robson and Sullivan[216]).

It also produces atrophy of the ovaries, hypertrophy of the breasts and such a variety of other effects that it is difficult to assess whether these are simply experimental curiosities. The question of interest is whether these are a result of powerful stimulation of smooth muscle in uterine vessels, placenta or umbilical vessels resulting in hypoxia of the embryo.

5. Endocardial Fibrotic Lesions

The term "endomyocardial fibrosis" is ordinarily used to describe the endocardial thickening occurring during what appears to be a specific disease, especially common in Africa but occasionally seen in northern countries. For example, I have seen only three such patients as compared with hundreds studied by physicians in Nigeria and Uganda. The fact that the disease is common in countries where serotonin-containing foods such as banana and plantain are eaten in large quantities, along with the fact that fibrosis occurs in the carcinoid syndrome, suggests a relationship between serotonin or its degradation products and the fibrotic lesions.

Attempts to reproduce the fibrosing endocardial lesions of man associated with carcinoid by daily injecting serotonin subcutaneously, or intraperitoneally, into animals even for as long a period as a year, seem to me naive. MacDonald[198] found the lesions so produced were only those of acute ischemia, such as resulted from *any* strong vasoconstrictor drug. This inadequate approach to the problem shows the need for a fresh look. Continuous administration of a substance in small amounts is much more likely to reproduce what happens in nature than single large injections of a metabolically active and labile substance.

The evidence in favor of the participation of serotonin in the genesis of fibrosis has been admirably summarized in a little-known paper by Hallén,[159] and the strongest case for its participation in man was made by Ojo and Parratt.[229] The disease occurs predominantly in Negroes whose diet contains large amounts of serotonin. It is rare in those areas of Africa where plantain and bananas are not habitually eaten. Lesions having some similarities with those in man can be produced in animals fed a plantain diet (McKinney and Crawford[206]).

Patients with endomyocardial fibrosis do not detoxify or excrete serotonin as effectively as do normal subjects. Ojo and Parratt point out that the disease is more likely to occur in populations when there is also protein malnutrition, parasitic infection, tuberculosis and chronic anemia. They suggest that serotonin derived from plantain is metabolized more slowly in poorly nourished subjects. Others such as Shaper[302] find no convincing evidence that the serotonin content of plantain is a factor in its etiology.

Furthermore, Selye[297] points out that there is experimental and morphological evidence that subendocardial necrosis may precede fibrosis. He conducted experiments in rats showing that brief periods of treatment with steroids such as 2-alpha-methyl-9-alpha-chlorocortisol, along with sodium acid phosphate, produce myocardial necrosis predominantly localized in the subendocardial layers. This healed with the formation of thick scar tissue resembling endomyocardial fibrosis. The cardiac necrosis was prevented by administering magnesium chloride and hence the secondary fibrosis did not develop. Whether this is an experimental counterpart of the clinical disease remains to be shown.

6. Effect on Fibrinolytic Activity and Thrombogenesis

Kwaan, Lo and McFadzean[190] observed in human subjects that intra- or para-venous injection of serotonin strongly stimulated fibrinolytic activity within veins. They suggested that platelet serotonin somehow helped initiate the mechanisms by which a clot in a vein is lysed. I do not understand this very interesting observation. It needs to be repeated and studied in depth.

Horton[172] investigated the possibility that reactive hyperemia might be due to liberation of kinins. Instead, he found that an increase in butanol-extractable serotonin occurred in the venous blood following circulatory arrest and release. No kinins were detected. He postulated that serotonin was released from platelets during the vascular occlusion and this led to increased fibrinolytic activity of the blood, so counteracting the tendency for coagulation to occur.

There is evidence both for and against the view that serotonin is released from platelets in the plug formed following injury of a vessel. Release is supposed to cause the vessel to contract around the thrombus to seal off the bleeding. Serotonin under some conditions also causes erythrocytes to aggregate, so increasing blood viscosity and possibly aiding clot formation, especially when blood flow is sluggish. Clearly, serotonin only abets the process of thrombogenesis.

No abnormality has been detected in the coagulation mechanism in patients whose platelet serotonin has been depleted by reserpine. However, this is not proof that serotonin has no effect. Milne and Cohn,[222] to the contrary, found that serotonin has an active role in blood coagulation.

A curious phenomenon has been noted by Selye, Tuckweber and Rohan[299] in which intravenous injection of various metals such as scandium chloride or sulfated polysaccharides, followed in 1 minute by subcutaneous or intravenous administration of serotonin, resulted within 24 hours in multiple hemorrhages and micro-thrombi resembling the Sanarelli-Shwartzman phenomenon. If small doses were used, the lesions occurred topically at the site of the challenge, but if large amounts were given lesions occurred in distant organs such as the kidneys, again quite similar to the generalized Sanarelli-Shwartzman reaction. The phenomenon was not specific for serotonin, since epinephrine and norepinephrine also elicited it.

Still another strange activity of serotonin appears in conjunction with its release by infused thrombin. Intravascular aggregation of erythrocytes occur. This was prevented if cyproheptadine, an inhibitor of serotonin and histamine, were given before the thrombin. Injected serotonin itself seems to increase aggregation of blood elements to the point of obstructing blood flow in, for example, the blood vessels of the conjunctiva (Swank, Fellman and Hissen[326]).

7. Serotonin and Phenylketonuria

The fundamental biochemical defect in phenylketonuria is failure of hydroxylation of phenylalanine to tyrosine. But also an association has been found between the high levels of phenylalanine in the plasma of phenylketonuric children and a decrease in serotonin. As early as 1954, Armstrong and Robinson[15] had found what they viewed as abnormal indole derivatives in the urine of phenylketonurics. There is marked reduction in excretion of serotonin, 5-hydroxyindoleacetic acid and tryptamine (Pare, Sandler and Stacey[248]). In a large number of patients, they[247] confirmed the finding of low serum serotonin and urinary 5-hydroxyindoleacetic acid but found no relationship between serotonin levels and intelligence. These chemical abnormalities were reduced by a low-phenylalanine diet, suggesting to them that 5-hydroxytryptophan decarboxylase might be inhibited by abnormal metabolites of phenylalanine. In such patients there may also be a decrease in dopamine, norepinephrine and epinephrine.

Evidence of a substantial sort is accumulating to show impaired maze performance following administration of excessive dietary phenylalanine. Addition of tryptophan improved the performance. High blood levels of leucine have been associated in human beings with severe mental retardation. Phenylalanine and leucine reduce serotonin levels in brain while tryptophan increases them. McKean, Schanberg and Giarman[205] have shown, in short, that maze performance is correlated with the cerebral content of serotonin by finding poor performance in weanling rats fed high dietary supplements of L-phenylalanine and L-leucine and superior performance with L-tryptophan. Adding tryptophan to the high phenylalanine diet reversed the behavioral defect. The brain serotonin concentration was 89 per cent of the control while feeding phenylalanine, 87 per cent with leucine and 14 per cent with tryptophan. This all seems consistent with the view that there is abnormal indole metabolism in phenylketonuric rats.

High phenylalanine diets in rats caused decreased concentrations of serotonin in brain. Yuwiler, Geller and Slater[362] found the most likely mechanism to be inhibition of precursor transport by phenylalanine although inhibition of tryptophan hydroxylation and decreased serotonin binding could not be excluded as possible mechanisms.

Freedland, Wadzinski and Waisman's[125] observation that rat's hepatic phenylalanine hydroxylase activity *decreases* on feeding excess phenylalanine and *increases* from excess tryptophan suggests a relationship.

Untreated phenylketonuric patients excreted less serotonin and 5-hydroxyindoleacetic acid in their urine than did those with mongolism and normal adults.[252] This difference was accentuated by oral administration of tryptophan. The phenylketonuric subjects excreted relatively large amounts of serotonin compared with controls. After their serum phenylalanine concentration had been reduced to normal level by a low-phenylalanine diet, the phenylketonuric subjects spontaneously excreted normal amounts of serotonin and 5-hydroxyindoleacetic acid.

A reversible defect in the 5-hydroxylation of tryptophan thus seems primarily responsible for the decreased production of serotonin in phenylketonuria.

8. Radioprotection and Liberation

Many papers have shown that serotonin protects against the lethal hemorrhagic effects of total body irradiation as well as causing liberation of it from the brain (literature in Garattini and Valzelli[135] and Palaić and Supek[246]). I know little about this subject and mention it to call attention to another of the bizarre actions of this substance.

The exact relationship of these findings to the occurrence of radiation sickness is an important unsolved problem in this syndrome.

9. Serotonin-Induced Abortion and Renal Cortical Thrombosis

Serotonin injected intraperitoneally into pregnant rats induces abortion and extensive glomerular thrombosis, according to Waugh and Pearl.[348] The cause of the abortion might be hypoxia elicited by vasoconstriction in the maternal circulation. The degenerative and hypoxic lesions of the placenta occurred as early as 2 hours after the injection, and within 6 hours hemorrhages were found in the decidua. Studies with India ink showed decreased circulation in the placenta and maternal renal vessels (Craig[85]).

Renal cortical necrosis resulting from serotonin had been first shown by E. W. Page and Glendening.[234]

10. Anti-Mouse Tumor Effect

Crile[87] has shown that serotonin injected repeatedly into melanomas implanted on hybrid mice feet inhibited the growth of the tumors and selectively destroyed some of them without damaging the feet. Also intratumor injections destroyed metastases of sarcoma growing in lymph nodes of mice. While histamine alone failed to inhibit growth of the tumors when added to serotonin, it appeared to augment the effectiveness of the latter. The mechanisms of these interesting actions are entirely unknown.

Papillomas elicited by painting the skin of mice with dimethylbenzanthracene were found by Riley and Shepherd[275] to contain serotonin, while the epidermis of both the control and treated mice contained tryptophan.

11. Serotonin as the Hyperglycemic Substance Released by Growth Hormone

Sirek, Geerling and Sirek[305] made the odd observation that serotonin may be the substance mediating the hyperglycemia resulting from administration of growth hormone. Normal dogs were injected with bovine growth hormone, blood removed after 40 minutes from the pancreaticoduodenal vein and immediately injected into fasting depancreatized dogs. Hyperglycemia resulted which could be prevented by 2-bromo-d-lysergic acid diethylamide, suggesting the mediator of the hyperglycemia to be serotonin.

12. Effect of Drinking Alcohol

The percentage of total C^{14} excreted as 5-hydroxyindoleacetic acid-C^{14} decreased by about half and the percentage of 5-hydroxytryptophol rose from about 2 to 42 when alcohol was administered 1 hour before giving the test dose of C^{14}-serotonin. The lowered 5-hydroxyindoleacetic acid excretion did not result from decreased monoamine oxidation, but from diversion of the intermediate 5-hydroxyindole and aldehyde to 5-hydroxytryptophol. The decrease was accounted for by the increase in 5-hydroxytryptophol excreted as the glucuronide and sulfate conjugates. The percentage of free C^{14}-5-hydroxytryptophol excreted in the urine was unchanged after ingestion of alcohol. Davis, Brown, Huff and Cashaw[90] showed this and suggested that alcohol causes a shift in serotonin metabolism from the oxidative pathway to the reductive one with 5-hydroxytryptophol formation.

Feldstein, Hoagland, Wong and Freeman[120] fed alcohol to healthy men and showed that it partially blocked the metabolism of radioactive serotonin to 5-hydroxyindoleacetic acid. They suggested, however, that alcohol apparently blocked monoamine oxidase or aldehyde dehydrogenase.

Olson, Gursey and Vester[230] had previously reported a reduction of 5-hydroxyindoleacetic acid in urine of chronic alcoholics, and Gursey, Vester and Olson[153] that the serotonin content of the brain stem of rabbits was depleted by alcohol. Others have found different results. The problem is complex, important and needs much creative investigation which, so far as I know, it is not receiving.

The most remarkable observation associating brain serotonin with alcohol is that of Myers and Veale.[224a] They found repeated microinfusions of minute amounts of alcohol into the cerebral ventricles of unrestrained rats produce a dose-dependent preference for alcohol. This preference was significantly reduced or totally abolished by oral p-chlorophenyl-alanine, the tryptophan hydroxylase inhibitor that selectively depletes brain serotonin. Some aversion to alcohol was noted while the inhibitor was being administered, but the rat's rejection of it was even more marked after the drug was discontinued. As a control, oral administration of alpha-methyl-p-tyrosine, a tyrosine hydroxylase inhibitor that depletes brain catecholamines, slightly reduced alcohol preference but it returned to normal as soon as the inhibitor was discontinued.

13. Carcinoids

The carcinoid is an argentaffin cell tumor usually with the primary lesion in the ileum but may be found in a variety of organs such as stomach and pancreas. It was described by a friend of mine, Prof. S. Oberndorfer[227] of my Munich days. For many years it was considered to produce no signs or symptoms other than those due to obstruction of the bowel. Upon discovery of serotonin, the associated clinical syndrome was described first in 1953.

In 1952, Biörck, Axén and Thorson[36] described a patient with metastatic carcinoid and pulmonic stenosis but without suggesting a causal relationship. Isler and Hedinger[176] proposed that there was a definite syndrome caused by the tumor and, in the same year, Lembeck[194] succeeded in extracting large amounts of serotonin from such tumors. By 1954, Thorson, Biörck, Bjorkman and Waldenström[330] described the clinical picture with detail and confidence. It was characterized by the singular violaceous flush, colic, diarrhea, bronchoconstriction and, at times, fibrosis of the endocardium, chiefly on the right but occasionally on both sides of the heart. Waldenström and his associates believe the symptoms and signs result primarily from excess serotonin. Liver metastases have usually occurred when signs and symptoms appear, probably indicating that serotonin may directly enter hepatic venous blood without being exposed to the destructive action of hepatic parenchyma. The wide variety of clinical manifestations are described most thoroughly by Sjoerdsma and Melmon[307] and by Grahame-Smith.[149] Gowenlock and Platt[146] have ably reviewed the clinical chemistry.

Certainly the most entertaining description of the syndrome was given by Bean and Funk,[28] in which ". . . the dazzling cutaneous regalia of flagrant changes in skin with a harlequin masquerade of colors said to mimic in clinical miniature the fickle phantasmagory of the Aurora Borealis." And again, "The many functions of serotonin are beginning to be explored along lines with much interest and enchantment for the clinician," ending with the postscript

> "This man was addicted to moanin',
> Confusion, edema and groanin',
> Intestinal rushes,
> Great tricolored blushes,
> And died from too much serotonin."

The cardiac lesion is a singular one consisting of collections of a peculiar type of fibrous tissue deposited upon the endocardium of the valvular cusps and cardiac chambers, especially on the right side, and upon the great veins, coronary sinus and occasionally the great arteries. Left-sided lesions are more common than initially believed. The distinguishing clinical feature is the presence of a murmur suggestive of tricuspid regurgitation or pulmonic stenosis. Elastic fibers are completely absent from this tissue. The cusps and mural endocardium are clearly separated from the fibrosing process by the endocardial elastic membrane. The fibrous material seems to be deposited from the blood. In this it may resemble what some investigators believe to be one of the important mechanisms involved in the formation of atherosclerotic plaques. No adequate experiment has yet been conducted to determine whether the lesion is due to serotonin or not.

The precursor relationship of dietary tryptophan to 5-hydroxyindoles in man was demonstrated by metabolic balance and tracer studies in patients with carcinoid. Sjoerdsma, Weissbach and Udenfriend[309] found as much as 60 per cent of dietary tryptophan is converted to urinary 5-hydroxyindoles in this disorder in contrast to about 1 per cent in normal persons.

The causes of the flush are still uncertain. Schneckloth, Page, Del Greco and Corcoran[295] found that it could be elicited by intravenous norepinephrine. Robertson, Peart and Andrews[278] were unable to correlate flush with the serotonin content of the blood. Then, in 1964, Oates, Melmon, Sjoerdsma, Gillespie and Mason[225] found that intravenous bradykinin caused flushes similar to those of carcinoid and, further, that extracts of hepatic metastases contained kallikrein, while extracts of normal liver did not. The colic and diarrhea probably are due to serotonin, since they are mimicked in normal persons by its infusion. Since bradykinin and kallidin are liberated by catecholamines, the flush initiated by norepinephrine may, in part, be mediated by one of these peptides. Mason and Melmon[218] and Grahame-Smith[149] recently summarized the evidence and supported the case for bradykinin. The production of bradykinin in the body probably has the following sequential steps:

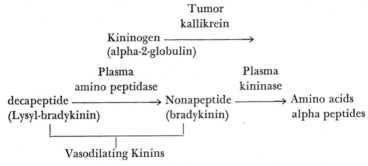

There are many variants of this clinical syndrome. Pernow and Waldenström[251] and Sandler and Snow[286] described patients with gastric carcinoid showing distinctive flushes, elevated urinary histamine and 5-hydroxytryptophan instead of serotonin. Oates and Sjoerdsma[226] had a similar patient. The serotonin content of the platelets was normal as was the excretion of 5-hydroxyindoleacetic acid. The increased histamine excretion did not appear related to elevated tissue concentrations of 5-hydroxytryptophan or serotonin.

Grahame-Smith[148] showed the presence of a stereospecific tryptophan hydroxylating system in carcinoid tumors which is not present in liver. He found it unlike the phenylalanine-hydroxylating system occurring in rat's liver.

Carcinoid is recognized by the characteristically increased excretion of 5-hydroxyindoleacetic acid, as measured by the method of Udenfriend, Titus and Weissbach.[339]

Page, Corcoran, Udenfriend, Sjoerdsma and Weissbach[241] described the usefulness of this measurement in a series of patients with carcinoid. Another major metabolite of serotonin was shown by Kveder, Iskrić and Keglević[189] to be the 6-glucuronide of 5-hydroxytryptophol. It has been found in one patient with carcinoid.

The carcinoid syndrome appears also in patients with carcinoid-type bronchial adenomas. However, the cells do not give an argentaffin reaction even though they apparently contain serotonin (Sauer, Dearing and Flock[289]). Mattingly[219] first suggested a causal relationship of the syndrome and the occurrence of liver metastases from bronchial adenoma. Apparently it can occur in absence of metastases, although it usually does not. As a variant, Sandler, Scheuer and Watt[285] described a patient with a primary bronchial tumor and the carcinoid syndrome in whom 5-hydroxytryptophan was detected both in the tumor and the urine. The many puzzling relationships between clinical signs and symptoms and chemical metabolism are effectively described in a recent article by Sandler[134] and in an editorial in Lancet.[101]

We have usually found chlorpromazine to be the most useful therapeutic agent to reduce the incidence of flushing attacks. A variety of agents supposedly blocking the actions of serotonin or bradykinin have been used with only uncertain success. These are phentolamine, methyldopa, methylsergide. Trasylol, a specific blocker of bradykinin, is ineffective. In a preliminary report by Engelman, Lovenberg and Sjoerdsma,[104] p-chlorophenylalanine has been used in 5 patients with carcinoid. Only one-fifth of the dose needed to produce biochemical effects in normal persons was used. Less flushing was noted for several days, diarrhea was lessened and, after a week, the 5-hydroxyindoleacetic acid excretion was reduced.

One of the many lessons to be learned from study of the carcinoid tumors is that careful and systematic clinical description of signs and symptoms in patients is a method we still have not fully mastered. It is hard to believe that this striking syndrome went so long unidentified. Perhaps another lesson is that nature usually provides a functioning tumor secreting substance of physiological significance. I know of no tumor that secretes a substance foreign to the body. Tumors have been both extraordinary guideposts and pedagogic crutches to clinicians as well as interesting biochemists sufficiently so that they documented the synthesis and degradation of the secretory products. But usually all of this occurs *after* the secreted product had been identified from other sources.

Another lesson is that it is always dangerous to attribute an entire syndrome to one substance or mechanism. While serotonin is doubtless intimately involved in the carcinoid system, there is good evidence that bradykinin is also concerned, probably both to varying degrees. But there may be a third and fourth substance as well.

14. The Dumping Syndrome

The similarities between the signs of the dumping syndrome and those of hyperserotonemia have suggested an etiologic relationship. The syndrome occurs in some patients after gastrectomy and is characterized by flushing, tachycardia, palpitation, weakness, syncope and feeling of warmth. The gastrointestinal symptoms include epigastric discomfort, borborygmus, nausea, vomiting and explosive diarrhea.

The evidence concerning the participation of serotonin has recently been reviewed by Reichle, Brigham and Rosemond[271] and by Tobe, Kimura and Fujiwara.[331] Consistent increase of serotonin in peripheral blood levels was found when 14 patients with the dumping syndrome were given *hypertonic* glucose orally while control patients showed no increase. Reichle, Brigham and Rosemond are convinced the release of serotonin into the blood stream accompanies the dumping syndrome but whether the amounts released are sufficient to account for all the signs remains to be determined.

Since the dumping syndrome also resembles both the intestinal and vasomotor signs of carcinoid, a search for bradykinin-like activity has been made by Zeitlin and Smith.[363] They were unable to find a significant increase in circulating serotonin, although the daily excretion of

5-hydroxyindoleacetic acid was raised. During the vasomotor signs of dumping, a release of bradykinin-like material and a fall in plasma kininogen occurred.

From the experimental viewpoint, impressive evidence has recently been published by Bennett, Bucknell and Dean[30] showing that, using Vane's rat fundus strip preparation, serotonin can be shown to be released into the lumen of the intact isolated rat stomach. Release of serotonin increased when the pressure within the stomach was raised or when the body-antrum preparation was stretched. The increase was not prevented by hexamethonium, atropine or procaine in doses that prevented peristalsis in response to transmural stimulation. Serotonin did not appear to be essential for gastric peristalsis in rats.

15. Migraine Headache

Several years ago, Sicuteri[300] noted that breakdown products of serotonin and norepinephrine were increased in amount in urine of patients experiencing an attack of migraine. Recently, Lance, Anthony and Gonski[191] showed that serotonin has a strong constrictor effect on extracranial arteries and that the total plasma serotonin level falls sharply at the onset of the attack and remains low during the headache. Serotonin levels did not change in patients with headache and vomiting, following air encephalography. Thus, the fall in serotonin levels is not due to stress (Anthony, Hinterberger and Lance[13]). If reserpine was administered, serotonin fell and a typical migraine headache occurred in susceptible subjects. Quite amazingly, the injection of serotonin then appeared to ameliorate both the spontaneous and reserpine-induced headache (Freedman[126]).

It is suggested that serotonin and possibly norepinephrine exert a tonic constrictor effect upon scalp arteries. If this humoral stimulation is withdrawn, these arteries dilate to elicit migraine headache (Lance, Anthony and Hinter-berger[192]).

16. Down's Syndrome

Older children with trisomy-21 type of Down's syndrome have depressed levels of whole-blood serotonin, and Bazelon, Paine, Cowie, Hunt, Houck and Mahanand[27] have recently also found the same in newborns with mongolism. Since this suggested a disturbed metabolism of serotonin, an attempt was made to elevate the low levels by feeding 5-hydroxytryptophan to 14 infants with mongolism. The hypotonia was greatly improved but no prognostic inferences about intelligence seemed justified. These interesting preliminary observations are now being continued in a double-blind study at the Children's Hospital of the District of Columbia. Rosner, Ong, Paine and Mahanand[282] also found significantly lower serotonin activity in blood of patients with trisomic Down's syndrome, as did Tu and Zellweger,[334] who, in addition, noted the lack of response to L-tryptophan loads, and a significant fall in serotonin level after administration of DL-penicillamine. They suggest that in patients with Down's syndrome, decarboxylation of 5-hydroxytryptophan is depressed.

17. Response to Injury

There is a growing literature partially reviewed by Asboe-Hansen[16] that serotonin is involved in injury response. He suggested that in human beings serotonin may function in the process of connective tissue repair and regeneration. Spector and Willoughby[318] had found significant amounts of serotonin in exudates formed by injecting two portions into rats. The increased capillary permeability seemed to be caused by the serotonin. Asboe-Hansen and Wegelius[17] had already shown the degranulating effect of serotonin upon mast cells. Evidently increase in capillary permeability varies widely in different animal species. Thus, Sparrow and Wilhelm[316] found serotonin highly potent in rats, being 11 times as active as histamine. But, in guinea pigs, its potency is negligible.

Both histamine and serotonin seem to be involved in the reaction of rats to injury even though not in shock. Sanyal and West[288] found the amine content of injured skin elevated, indicating mobilization from tissue mast cells after aseptic injury. Healing was greatly delayed if the skin had been de- pleted of serotonin and histamine but enhanced by treatment with heparin, another constituent of tissue mast cells. In the exudative and reparative phases of inflammation, depletion also adversely affects healing. They suggested that serotonin was the more important amine in inflammation since it stimulates phagocytosis.

The effect of serotonin on the small blood vessels in a chamber inserted into a rabbit's ear has been studied by Ebert and Graham.[99] It did not elicit the early inflammatory changes seen after histamine, although early and relatively prolonged arteriolar dilatation occurred. The most striking effect was the formation of multiple venular platelet-leuko- cyte thromboemboli.

Much evidence had suggested that chemically dissimilar agents such as serotonin, histamine and bradykinin all cause blood vessels to leak through submicroscopic gaps that appear between the endothelial cells. The most plausible theory to explain the appearance of the gap was that increase in pres- sure was caused by constriction of the veins. If the larger veins contract, blood pressure in the venules rises. Majno, Gilmore and Leventhal[207] tested this hypothesis on vessels of an exposed striated muscle of anesthetized rats and rabbits given a neuromuscular blocking agent. The leak mediator was injected and leakage estimated from intravenously in- jected carbon black. Constriction of a small vein was rare, hence they conclude that venous spasm cannot account for the leakage. The alternative hypothesis is suggested that leakage-mediators cause leakage by a direct effect on venular endothelium which is induced to contract.

When much less artificial conditions are imposed and dogs used, McCubbin, Kaneko and Page[202] found that electrical stimulation of sympathetic pathways caused venoconstriction of the mesenteric vessels which was relaxed by intra-arterial injection of serotonin. Without stimulation, serotonin alone caused constriction of both large and small arteries as well as veins. These experiments show that serotonin affects the caliber of the venous system when the nerves are intact but tell us nothing about the effects on vascular leakage which may be quite different from the experiments of Majno, Gilmore and Leventhal, in which the neural mechanisms were blocked.

Whole body x-radiation with high doses increases the serotonin content of rat and mice brain (see p. 102).

18. Audiogenic Seizures

Strains of mice have been bred that are extremely susceptible to audiogenic seizures. The serotonin content of brains of such animals was found significantly lower than mice resistant to such attacks (Schlesinger, Boggan and Freedman[294]). Further, the difference was found only at about 21 days of age, which corresponded with the time of maximal seizure susceptibility. Norepinephrine was also reduced. The mechanistic association of this reduction in amines and the seizures is unknown.

CHAPTER 6

An Overview

OUT OF THE many thousands of studies on serotonin and related indolealkylamines, what generalization can reasonably be drawn? Perhaps Shakespeare anticipated us all when he wrote, "Sweet are the uses of adversity; which, like the toad, ugly and venomous, wears yet a precious jewel in his head" (*As You Like It,* Act II, Scene I). Did he not refer to the toad's parotoid gland so rich in these substances? He might have added that the skin of *Bufo alvaris,* a toad from Arizona, also contains one of the richest known collections, including 5-methoxy- and sulfur-containing derivatives of serotonin, as well. But then the Bard never visited Arizona, where the toad quite wisely lives!

One of the most striking characteristics of the indolealkylamines is their highly specific distribution. Parotoid glands, skin and mast cells of only certain species, some kinds of enterochromaffin cells, certain unrelated plants, the pineal region, serotonergic neurons, blood platelets, pinealomas, carcinoid tumors and defense mechanisms in both animals and plants—all are rich in them.

It should be noted that the enzyme systems are widely distributed for the synthesis and destruction of these substances; many cells may synthesize them without storage, which would make their demonstration much more difficult.

The nervous system seems to keep its indolealkylamines

largely to itself, synthesizing and metabolizing them. They are stored in synaptic vesicles which may have their counterpart in blood platelets.

They tend to associate themselves with the catecholamines in nerve tissues but still occupy different anatomical areas. It is as though, like most monoamines, they service similar but not identical functions. They seem to appear in greater abundance earlier in the phylogenetic scale.

Evidence is accumulating that they have transmitter function in the nervous system, stimulate gastrointestinal propulsion, aid in cardiovascular control, participate in the mechanisms of inflammation and of cellular proliferation, and in the defense mechanisms of certain animals and plants and are part of the rhythmic physiological control mechanisms in the pineal region. Serotonin seems to have a hormonal action much the same in carbohydrate metabolism in invertebrates that epinephrine does in higher organisms. It increases formation of cyclic $3',5'$-AMP, phosphorylase activation, stimulation of glycogenolysis and of glycolysis.

All these functions seem to fit under the general heading of being "regulatory." They aid the organism in adapting to its changing environment.

Serotonin is the most ubiquitous of the indolealkylamines, but a variety of derivatives also are synthesized within the body for special functions and under abnormal conditions. Like the catecholamines, these substances serve many functions, indicating the extraordinary economy with which the body uses chemical regulating substances. Unlike the enzyme, they appear to have a low grade of specificity and there is some suggestive evidence that monoamines may occasionally substitute for one another.

The indolealkylamines are a widespread class of substances with newly appreciated qualities which place them alongside the catecholamines as regulatory substances aiding in the electrochemical control of cellular function. Their distribution, synthesis and destruction, transport and adaptability all suggest their control of functions of the nervous system, the gastrointestinal tract and cardiovascular system may be obligate but are usually facultative. As has often been true, the discovery of a new group of biogenic substances brings descriptions of new disease syndromes, and serotonin has been no exception.

Serotonin has added yet another facet to the equilibrated system which controls many bodily functions. In disease states, it and its derivatives will be detected and measured because of their abnormal amounts, but in normal circumstances it seems to take its part with other substances in an orderly fashion, scarcely displaying the multiplicity of actions that so delight the pharmacologist and biochemist.

Bibliography

1. Aghajanian, G. K., Bloom, F. E., Lovell, R. A., Sheard, M. H., and Freedman, D. X.: The uptake of 5-hydroxytryptamine-^{3}H from the cerebral ventricles: Autoradiographic localization, Biochem. Pharmacol. 15: 1401, 1966.
2. ———, Rosencrans, J. A., and Sheard, M. H.: Serotonin: Release in the forebrain by stimulation of midbrain raphe, Science 156:402, 1967.
3. Aiello, E., and Guideri, G.: Relationship between 5-hydroxytryptamine and nerve stimulation of ciliary activity, J. Pharmacol. & Exper. Therap. 154:517, 1966.
4. Amin, A. H., Crawford, T. B. B., and Gaddum, J. H.: The distribution of substance P and 5-hydroxytryptamine in the central nervous system of the dog, J. Physiol. 126:596, 1954.
5. Andén, N. E., Corrodi, H., Dahlström, A., Fuxe, K., and Hökfelt, T.: Effects of tyrosine hydroxylase inhibition on the amine levels of central monoamine neurons, Life Sc. 5:561, 1966.
6. ———, Corrodi, H., Fuxe, K., and Hökfelt, T.: Evidence for a central 5-hydroxytryptamine receptor stimulation by lysergic acid diethylamide, Brit. J. Pharmacol. (In press.)
7. ———, Dahlström, A., Fuxe, K., and Larsson, K.: Mapping out of catecholamine and 5-hydroxytryptamine neurons innervating the telencephalon and diencephalon, Life Sc. 4:1275, 1965.
8. ———, Fuxe, K., and Hökfelt, T.: The importance of the nervous impulse flow for the depletion of the monoamines from central neurons by some drugs, J. Pharm. & Pharmacol. 18:630, 1966.
9. ———, Fuxe, K., and Hökfelt, T.: Effect of some drugs on central monoamine terminals lacking nerve impulse flow, European J. Pharmacol. 1: 226, 1967.
10. ———, and Magnusson, T.: An improved method for the fluorimetric determination of 5-hydroxytryptamine in tissue, Acta physiol. scandinav. 69:87, 1967.
11. ———, Magnusson, T., Roos, B.-E., and Werdinius, B.: 5-Hydroxyindoleacetic acid of rabbit spinal cord normally and after transection, Acta physiol. scandinav. 64:193, 1965.
12. Anderson, B., Jobin, M., and Olsson, K.: Serotonin and temperature control, Acta physiol. scandinav. 67:50, 1966.

13. Anthony, M., Hinterberger, H., and Lance, J. W.: Plasma serotonin in migraine and stress, Arch. Neurol. 16:544, 1967.
14. Antopol, W., and Chryssanthou, C.: Shwartzman phenomenon mechanisms: Newer concepts, Arch. Path. 78:313, 1964.
15. Armstrong, M. D., and Robinson, K. S.: On the excretion of indole derivatives in phenylketonuria, Arch. Biochem. 52:287, 1954.
16. Asboe-Hansen, G.: Hormone control of connective tissue, Fed. Proc. 25: 1136, 1966.
17. ———, and Wegelius, O.: Serotonin and connective tissue, Nature, London 178:262, 1956.
18. Ashcroft, G. W., Eccleston, D., Crawford, T. B. B., Sharman, D. F., MacDougall, E. J., Stanton, J. B., and Binns, J. K.: 5-Hydroxyindole compounds in the cerebrospinal fluid of patients with psychiatric or neurological diseases, Lancet 2:1049, 1966.
19. Axelrod, J.: Control of catecholamine and indoleamine metabolism by sympathetic nerves. From *Mechanisms of Release of Biogenic Amines,* Pergamon Press, New York, 1966, p. 189.
20. ———, and Inscoe, J. K.: The uptake and binding of circulating serotonin and the effect of drugs, J. Pharmacol. & Exper. Therap. 141:161, 1963.
21. ———, and Weissbach, H.: Enzymatic O-methylation of N-acetylserotonin to melatonin, Science 131:1312, 1960.
22. ———, and Wurtman, R. J.: The formation, metabolism and some actions of melatonin, a pineal gland substance. In "Endocrines and the central nervous system," 43, 200, 1966.
23. Bailey, I. S.: Cyproheptadine in treatment of urticaria, Brit. M. J. 2:430, 1961.
24. Barchas, J. D., and Freedman, D. X.: Brain amines: Response to physiological stress, Biochem. Pharmacol. 12:1225, 1963.
25. Bartholini, G., Pletscher, A., and Bruderer, H.: Formation of 5-hydroxytryptophol from endogenous 5-hydroxytryptamine by isolated blood platelets, Nature, London 203:1, 281, 1964.
26. Bartlet, A. L.: The influence of chlorpromazine on the metabolism of 5-hydroxytryptamine in the mouse, Brit. J. Pharmacol. 24:497, 1965.
27. Bazelon, M., Paine, R. S., Cowie, V. A., Hunt, P., Houck, J. C., and Mahanand, D.: Reversal of hypotonia in infants with Down's syndrome by administration of 5-hydroxytryptophan, Lancet 1:1130, 1967.
28. Bean, W. B., and Funk, D.: The vasculocardiac syndrome of metastatic carcinoid, Arch. Int. Med. 103:189, 1959.
29. Benditt, E. P., Wong, R. L., Arase, M., and Roeper, E.: 5-Hydroxytryptamine in mast cells, Proc. Soc. Exper. Biol. & Med. 90:303, 1955.
30. Bennett, A., Bucknell, A., and Dean, A. C. B.: The release of 5-hydroxytryptamine from the rat stomach in vitro, J. Physiol. 182:57, 1966.
31. Bennett, D. S., and Giarman, N. J.: Schedule of appearance of 5-hydroxytryptamine (serotonin) and associated enzymes in the developing rat brain, J. Neurochem. 12:911, 1965.
32. Bertie, F., and Shore, P. A.: A kinetic analysis of drugs that inhibit the adrenergic neuronal membrane amine pump, Biochem. Pharmacol. 16:2091, 1967.
33. Bertler, A., Falck, B., and Owman, C.: Studies on 5-hydroxytryptamine stores in pineal gland of rat, Acta physiol. scandinav. 63: (supp. 239)1, 1964.
34. Bhattacharya, B. K., and Lewis, G. P.: Comparison of the effect of re-

serpine and 48/80 on the histamine and 5-hydroxytryptamine in mast cells of rats, J. Physiol. 133:10, 1956.

35. ———, and Lewis, G. P.: The release of 5-hydroxytryptamine by histamine liberators, Brit. J. Pharmacol. 11:202, 1956.

36. Biörck, G., Axén, O., and Thorson, Å.: Unusual cyanosis in a boy with congenital pulmonary stenosis and tricuspid insufficiency. Fatal outcome after angiocardiography, Am. Heart J. 44:143, 1952.

37. Blaschko, H., Born, G. V. R., D'Iorio, A., and Eade, N. R.: Sedimentation of adrenal medullary granules in hypertonic sucrose, J. Physiol. 132:44, 1956.

38. Bloom, F. E., Costa, E., and Salmoiraghi, G. C.: Analysis of individual rabbit olfactory bulb neuron responses to the microelectrophoresis of acetylcholine, norepinephrine and serotonin synergists and antagonists, J. Pharmacol. & Exper. Therap. 146:16, 1964.

39. Bock, K. D., Dengler, H., Kuhn, H. M., and Matthes, K.: Effect of 5-hydroxytryptamine on blood pressure and blood circulation in skin and muscles in humans, Arch. exper. Path. u. Pharmakol. 230:257, 1957.

40. Bogdanski, D. F., Pletscher, A., Brodie, B. B., and Udenfriend, S.: Identification and assay of serotonin in brain, J. Pharmacol. & Exper. Therap. 117:82, 1956.

41. ———, Weissbach, H., and Udenfriend, S.: Pharmacological studies with the serotonin precursor, 5-hydroxytryptophan, J. Pharmacol. & Exper. Therap. 122:182, 1958.

42. Bondi, T., Siegler, P. E., Brown, E. B., Gershenfeld, M. A., and Nodine, J. H.: Clinical use of a new antihistamine and antiserotonin drug: Cyproheptadine, Ann. Allergy 19:386, 1961.

43. Born, G. V. R.: Changes in the distribution of phosphorus in platelet-rich plasma during clotting, Biochem. J. 68:695, 1958.

44. ———, Ingram, G. I. C., and Stacey, R. S.: The relationship between 5-hydroxytryptamine and adenosine triphosphate in blood platelets, Brit. J. Pharmacol. 13:62, 1958.

45. Boucek, R. J., Boucek, R. J., Jr., Hlavackova, V., and Dietrich, L. S.: Tryptophan metabolism during the mid-period of embryonic development (chick), Biochem. et biophys. acta 141:473, 1967.

46. Boullin, D. J.: Observations on the significance of 5-hydroxytryptamine in relation to the peristaltic reflex of the rat, Brit. J. Pharmacol. 23:14, 1964.

47. Brinkhous, K. M.: Basic mechanisms of cell adhesion and platelet thrombosis formation, Fed. Proc. 26:84, 1967.

48. Brodie, B. B., Bogdanski, D. F., and Bonomi, L.: Formation, storage and metabolism of serotonin (5-hydroxytryptamine) and catecholamines in lower vertebrates, Proc. 5th Internat. Neurochem. Symp., St. Wolfgang, Austria, 1962, p. 367.

49. ———, Comer, M. S., Costa, E., and Dlabac, A.: The role of brain serotonin in the mechanism of the central action of reserpine, J. Pharmacol. & Exper. Therap. 152:340, 1966.

50. ———, and Costa, E.: Some current views on brain monoamines. From *Monoamines et Systeime Nerveux Central*, Georg & Cie, Geneva, 1962.

51. ———, and Reid, W. D.: Serotonin in Brain: Functional Considerations, in *Advances in Pharmacology*, Academic Press, New York, 1968, Vol. 6A.

52. ———, and Shore, P. A.: On a Role for Serotonin and Norepinephrine as Chemical Mediators in the Central Autonomic Nervous System, in

Hormones, Brain, Function and Behavior, H. Hoagland (ed.), Academic Press, New York, 1957.

53. Brownlee, G., and Johnson, E. S.: The release of acetylcholine from the isolated ileum of the guinea-pig induced by 5-hydroxytryptamine and dimethylphenylpiperazinium, Brit. J. Pharmacol. 24:689, 1965.

53a. Buccino, R. A., Covell, J. R., Sonnenblick, E. H., and Braunwald, E.: Effects of serotonin on the contractile state of the myocardium, Am. J. Physiol. 213:483, 1967.

54. Buckingham, S., and Maynert, E. W.: The release of 5-hydroxytryptamine, potassium and amino acids from platelets, J. Pharmacol. & Exper. Therap. 143:332, 1964.

55. Bulat M., and Supek, Z.: The penetration of 5-hydroxytryptamine through the blood-brain barrier, J. Neurochem. 14:265, 1967.

56. Bülbring, E., and Crema, A.: Observations concerning the action of 5-hydroxytryptamine on the peristaltic reflex, Brit. J. Pharmacol. 13:444, 1958.

57. Bumpus, F. M., and Page, I. H.: Serotonin and its methylated derivatives in human urine, J. Biol. Chem. 212:111, 1955.

58. Burgen, A. S. V., and Kuffler, S. W.: Inhibition of the cardiac ganglion of Limulus polyphemus by 5-hydroxytryptamine, Biol. Bull. 113:336, 1956.

59. Burks, T. F., and Long, J. P.: 5-Hydroxytryptamine release into dog intestinal vasculature, Am. J. Physiol. 211:619, 1966.

60. Carlsson, A.: Functional significance of drug-induced changes in brain monoamine levels, Prog. Brain Res. 8:9, 1964.

61. ————: Drugs which Block the Storage of 5-Hydroxytryptamine and Related Amines, in *Handbook of Experimental Pharmacology,* O. Eichler and A. Farah (eds.), Springer, Berlin, 1965.

62. ————: Physiological and Pharmacological Release of Monoamines in the Central Nervous System, in *Mechanisms of Release of Biogenic Amines,* U. S. von Euler, S. Rosell and B. Uvnäs (eds.), Pergamon Press, New York, 1966.

63. ————: Modification of sympathetic function, Pharmacol. Rev. 18:541, 1966.

64. ————: *Handbuch der experimentellen Pharmakologie,* Springer Verlag, Berlin, Heidelberg, New York, 1966, p. 529.

65. ————, and Corrodi, H.: In den Catecholamin-Metabolismus eingreifende Substanzen. 3. 2,3-Dihydroxyphenylacetamide und verwandte Verbindungen, Helv. chim. acta 47:1340, 1964.

66. ————, Falck, B., Fuxe, K., and Hillarp, N. A.: Cellular localization of monoamines in the spinal cord, Acta physiol. scandinav. 60:112, 1964.

67. ————, Falck, B., and Hillarp, N. A.: Cellular localization of brain monoamines, Acta physiol. scandinav. 56:supp. 196, 1962.

68. ————, Fuxe, K., and Ungerstedt, U.: The effect of imipramine on central 5-hydroxytryptamine neurons, J. Pharm. & Pharmacol. 20:150, 1968.

69. ————, and Hillarp, N. A.: Kgl. Fysiograf. Sällskap. Lund, Förh. 26, 1956.

70. ————, and Lindqvist, M.: Effect of chlorpromazine or haloperidol on formation of 3-methoxytyramine and normetanephrine in mouse brain, Acta pharmacol. et toxicol. 20:140, 1963.

71. ————, and Lindqvist, M.: Metatyrosine as a tool for selective protection of catecholamine stores against reserpine, European J. Pharmacol. 2:187, 1967.

72. Chase, T. N., Breese, G. R., Carpenter, D. O., Schanberg, S. M., and Kopin, I. J.: Stimulation-induced Release of Serotonin, in *Advances in Pharmacology,* Academic Press, New York, 1968, Vol. 6A, p. 351.

73. ———, Breese, G. R., and Kopin, I. J.: Serotonin release from brain slices by electrical stimulation: Regional differences and effect of LSD, Science 157:1461, 1967.

74. Chiocchio, S. R., Biscardi, A. M., and Tramezzani, J. H.: 5-Hydroxytryptamine in the carotid body of the cat, Science 158:790, 1967.

75. Comroe, J. H., Jr., van Lingen, B., Stroud, R. C., and Roncorini, A.: Reflex and direct cardiopulmonary effects of 5-OH-tryptamine (serotonin); their possible role in pulmonary embolism and coronary thrombosis, Am. J. Physiol. 173:379, 1953.

76. ———, and Mortimer, L.: The respiratory and cardiovascular responses of temporally separated aortic and carotid bodies to cyanide, nicotine, phenyldiguanide and serotonin, J. Pharmacol. & Exper. Therap. 146:33, 1964.

77. Cooper, K. E., Cranston, W. I., and Honour, A. J.: Effects of intraventricular and intrahypothalamic injections of noradrenaline and 5-HT on body temperature in conscious rabbits, J. Physiol. 181:8521, 1965.

78. Coppen, A., Shaw, D. M., Herzberg, B., and Maggs, R.: Tryptophan in the treatment of depression, Lancet 2:1178, 1967.

79. Corne, S. J., Pickering, R. W., and Warner, B. T.: A method for assessing the effects of drugs on the central actions of 5-hydroxytryptamine, Brit. J. Pharmacol. 20:106, 1963.

80. Corrodi, H.: Blockade of the psychotic syndrome caused by nialamide in mice, J. Pharm. & Pharmacol. 18:197, 1966.

81. ———, Fuxe, K., and Hökfelt, T.: A possible role played by central monoamine neurons in thermo-regulation, Acta physiol. scandinav. 71:224, 1967.

82. Costa, E.: The role of serotonin in neurobiology, Internat. Rev. Neurobiol. 2:175, 1960. C. C. Pfeiffer and J. R. Smythies (eds.), Academic Press, New York, 1960.

83. ———, and Aprison, M. H.: Studies on the 5-hydroxytryptamine (serotonin) content in human brain, J. Nerv. & Ment. Dis. 126:289, 1958.

84. ———, Gessa, G. L., Hirsch, C., Kuntzman, R., and Brodie, B. B.: On current status of serotonin as a brain neurohormone and in action of reserpine-like drugs, Ann. New York Acad. Sc. 96:118, 1962.

85. Craig, J. M.: Mechanism of serotonin-induced abortion in rats, Arch. Path. 81:257, 1966.

86. Cremata, V. Y., and Koe, B. K.: Clinical pharmacological evaluation of p-chlorophenylalanine—a new serotonin-depleting agent, Clin. Pharmacol. & Therap. 7:768, 1966.

87. Crile, G. W., Jr.: Inhibition of growth of mouse tumors by injections of serotonin or serotonin and histamine combined, Cleveland Clin. Quart. 33:25, 1966.

88. Cunningham, D. J., Stolwijk, A. J., Murakami, N., and Hardy, J. D.: Responses of neurones in the preoptic area to temperature, serotonin and epinephrine, Am. J. Physiol. 123:1570, 1967.

89. Dahlström, A.: The intraneuronal distribution of noradrenaline and the transport and life-span of amine storage granules in the sympathetic adrenergic neuron, M. D. thesis, Karolinska Institute, Stockholm, 1966.

90. Davis, V. E., Brown, H., Huff, J. A., and Cashaw, J. L.: The alteration of serotonin metabolism to 5-hydroxytryptophol by ethanol ingestion in man, J. Lab. & Clin. Med. 69:132, 1967.

91. Denker, S. J., Malm, U., Roos, B.-E., and Werdinius, B.: Acid monoamine metabolites of cerebrospinal fluid in mental depression and mania, J. Neurochem. 13:1545, 1966.
92. De Robertis, E.: Ultrastructure and cytochemistry of the synaptic region, Science 156:907, 1967.
93. ———, and Bennett, H. S.: A submicroscopic vesicular component of Schwann cells and nerve satellite cells, Exper. Cell Res. 6:543, 1954.
94. Diaz, P., Ngai, S. H., and Costa, E.: The effect of LSD on the metabolism of rat brain serotonin (5-HT), Pharmacologist 9:251, 1967.
95. Dombro, R. S., and Woolley, D. W.: Cinnamanilides as structural analogs and antagonists of serotonin, Biochem. Pharmacol. 13:569, 1964.
96. Doyle, J. D.: The effect of an anti-serotonin on the bioluminescence of meganyctiphanes norvegica, J. Physiol. 186:92, 1966.
97. Dubnick, B., Rucki, E. W., and Phillips, G. E.: Selective lowering of brain serotonin (5-HT) by p-acylphenethylamines, Pharmacologist 9: 250, 1967.
98. Duteil, J. J., and Aviado, D. M.: Factors influencing pulmonary hypertensive response to 5-hydroxytryptamine, Circulation Res. 11:466, 1962.
99. Ebert, R. H., and Graham, R. C.: Observations on the effects of histamine and serotonin in the rabbit ear chamber, Angiology 17:402, 1966.
100. Eccleston, D., Moir, A. T. B., Reading, H. W., and Ritchie, I. M.: The formation of 5-hydroxytryptophol in brain in vitro, Brit. J. Pharmacol. 28:367, 1966.
101. Editorial: Lancet 1:404, 1968.
102. El Hawary, M. B. E., and Feldberg, W.: Effect of 5-hydroxytryptophan acting from the cerebral ventricles on 5-hydroxytryptamine output and body temperature, J. Physiol. 186:401, 1966.
103. ———, Feldberg, W., and Lotti, V. J.: Monoamine oxidase inhibitor: Effect of 5-hydroxytryptamine output from perfused third ventricle and body temperature, J. Physiol. 188:131, 1967.
104. Engelman, K., Lovenberg, W., and Sjoerdsma, A.: Inhibition of serotonin synthesis by para-chlorophenylalanine in patients with the carcinoid syndrome, New England J. Med. 277:1103, 1967.
105. Erspamer, V.: Pharmacology of indolealkylamines, Pharmacol. Rev. 6: 425, 1954.
106. ———: Some observations on the fate of exogenous 5-hydroxytryptamine (enteramine) in the rat, J. Physiol. 133:1, 1956.
107. ———: Recent research in the field of 5-hydroxytryptamine and related indole alkylamines, Fortschr. Artzneimittelforsch. 3:151, 1961.
108. ———: Recent Research in the Field of 5-Hydroxytryptamine and Related Indolealkylamines, in *Progress in Drug Research*, E. Jucker (ed.), Interscience Publishers, New York, 1961.
109. ———, and Asero, B.: Identification of enteramine, specific hormone of enterochromaffin system, as 5-hydroxytryptamine, Nature, London 169: 800, 1952.
110. ———, and Ghiretti, F.: The action on enteramine on the heart of molluscs, J. Physiol. 115:470, 1951.
111. ———, Vitali, T., Roseghini, M., and Cei, J. M.: 5-Methoxy- and 5-hydroxyindoles in the skin of Bufo alvaris, Biochem. Pharmacol. 16:1149, 1967.
112. von Euler, U. S., Rosell, S., and Uvnäs, B.: Mechanisms of release of biogenic amines, Pergamon Press, Oxford, 1966.

113. Fairman, M. D., and Heble, A.: Effect of oxygen-pressure interactions on cerebral norepinephrine (N.E.) and 5-hydroxytryptamine (5-HT), Pharmacologist 9:250, 1967.
114. Falck, B.: Cellular localization of monoamines, Prog. Brain Res. 8:28, 1964.
115. ————, and Owman, C.: 5-Hydroxytryptamine and related amines in endocrine cell systems, in *Advances in Pharmacology*, Academic Press, New York, 1968, Vol. 6A, p. 211.
116. ————, Owman, C. H., and Rosengren, E.: Changes in rat pineal stores of 5-hydroxytryptamine after inhibition of its synthesis or breakdown, Acta physiol. scandinav. 67:300, 1966.
117. Feldberg, W. S.: Transmission in the central nervous system and sensory transmission, Pharmacol. Rev. 6:85, 1954.
118. ————, and Myers, R. D.: Temperature changes produced by amines injected into the cerebral ventricles during anaesthesia, J. Physiol. 175:464, 1964.
119. ————, and Smith, A. N.: Release of histamine by tryptamine and 5-hydroxytryptamine, Brit. J. Pharmacol. 8:406, 1953.
120. Feldstein, A., Hoagland, H., Wong, K., and Freeman, H.: Biogenic amines, biogenic aldehydes and alcohol, Quart. J. Studies Alcohol 25:218, 1964.
121. Fink, M. A.: Anaphylaxis in the mouse: Possible relation of the Schultz-Dale reaction to serotonin release, Proc. Soc. Exper. Biol. & Med. 92:673, 1956.
122. Fischer, E., and Spatz, H.: Determination of bufotenin in the urine of schizophrenics, Internat. J. Neuropsych. 3:226, 1967.
123. Florey, E., and Florey, E.: Über die mögliche Bedeutung von Enteramin (5-oxy-Tryptamin) als nervöse Aktions-substanz bei cephalopoden und dekapoden Crustacean, Z. Naturforsch. 9:58, 1954.
124. Folkow, B., Häggendal, J., and Lisander, B.: Extent of release and elimination of noradrenaline at peripheral adrenergic nerve terminals, Acta physiol. scandinav., supp. 307, 1967.
125. Freedland, R. A., Wadzinski, I. M., and Waisman, H. A.: The enzymatic hydroxylations of tryptophan, Biochem. Biophys. Res. Commun. 5:94, 1961.
126. Freedman, D. X.: Effects of LSD-25 on brain serotonin, J. Pharmacol. & Exper. Therap. 134:160, 1961.
127. ————: Psychotomimetic drugs and brain biogenic amines, Am. J. Psychiat. 119:843, 1963.
128. ————: Aspects of the Biochemical Pharmacology of Psychotropic Drugs, in *Psychiatric Drugs*, Grune & Stratton, New York, 1966, p. 32.
129. ————, and Giarman, N. J.: Brain Amines, Electrical Activity and Behavior, Chap. 8, in *EEG and Behavior*, G. H. Glaser (ed.), Basic Books, 1963.
130. Fuxe, K., Hökfelt, T., and Ungerstedt, U.: Morphologic, pharmacologic and functional studies on 5-hydroxytryptamine neurons in the central nervous system of mammals, 5-HT Symposium, New York, May, 1967.
131. Fuxe, K., and Jousson, G.: A modification of the histochemical fluorescence method for the improved localization of 5-hydroxytryptamine, Histochemie 11:161, 1967.
132. Gaddum, J. H., and Giarman, N. J.: Preliminary studies on the biosynthesis of 5-hydroxytryptamine, Brit. J. Pharmacol. 11:88, 1956.

133. Gal, E. M., and Marshall, F. D., Jr.: The hydroxylation of tryptophan by pigeon brain in vivo, Prog. Brain Res. 8:56, 1964.
134. Garattini, S., Shore, P. A., Costa, E., and Sandler, M. (eds.): *Advances in Pharmacology,* Academic Press, New York, 1968, Vol. 6A.
135. Garattini, S., and Valzelli, L.: *Serotonin,* Elsevier, Amsterdam, 1965.
136. Gerschenfeld, H.-M., and Stefani, E.: 5-Hydroxytryptamine receptors and synaptic transmission in molluscan neurones, Nature, London 205:1216, 1965.
137. ———, and Stefani, E.: Evidence for an Excitatory Transmitter Role of Serotonin in Molluscan Central Synapse, in *Advances in Pharmacology,* Academic Press, New York, 1968, Vol. 6A, p. 369.
138. Gershon, M. D., Drakontides, A. B., and Ross, L. L.: Serotonin: Synthesis and release from the myenteric plexus of the mouse intestine, Science 149:197, 1965.
139. ———, and Ross, L. L.: Studies on the relationship of 5-hydroxytryptamine and the enterochromaffin cell to anaphylactic shock in mice, J. Exper. Med. 115:367, 1962.
140. ———, and Ross, L. L.: Radioisotopic studies of the binding, exchange and distribution of 5-hydroxytryptamine synthesized from its radioactive precursor, J. Physiol. 186:451, 1966.
141. ———, and Ross, L. L.: Location of sites of 5-hydroxytryptamine storage and metabolism by radioautography, J. Physiol. 186:477, 1966.
142. Gertner, S. B., Paasonen, M. K., and Giarman, N. J.: Studies concerning the presence of 5-hydroxytryptamine (serotonin) in the perfusate from the superior cervical ganglion, J. Pharmacol. & Exper. Therap. 127:268, 1959.
143. Giarman, N. J., and Day, M.: Presence of biogenic amines in the bovine pineal gland, Biochem. Pharmacol. 1:235, 1959.
144. ———, and Freedman, D. X.: Biochemical aspects of the action of psychotomimetic drugs, Pharmacol. Rev. 17:1, 1965.
145. Gluckman, M. I., Hart, E. R., and Marrazzi, A. S.: Cerebral synaptic inhibition by serotonin and iproniazide, Science 126:448, 1957.
146. Gowenlock, A. H., and Platt, D. S.: The Clinical Chemistry of Carcinoid Tumours, in *The Clinical Chemistry of Monoamines,* Varley, H., and Gowenlock, A. H. (eds.), 2:140, 1962, Elsevier, New York.
147. Grahame-Smith, D. G.: The enzymic conversion of tryptophan into 5-hydroxytryptophan by isolated brain tissue, Biochem. J. 92:52, 1964.
148. ———: Tryptophan hydroxylation in carcinoid tumors, Biochem. et biophys. acta 86:176, 1964.
149. ———: The carcinoid syndrome, Am. J. Cardiol. 21:376, 1968.
150. de Groat, W. C., and Ryall, R. W.: An excitatory action of 5-hydroxytryptamine on sympathetic preganglionic neurons, Exper. Brain Res. 3:299, 1967.
151. Groth, C. G.: Effect of infused thrombin on the tissue oxygen tension. II. The possible role of 5-hydroxytryptamine and histamine. An experimental study in the rabbit, Acta chir. scandinav. 132:15, 1966.
152. Guroff, G., Daly, J. W., Jerina, D. M., Renson, J., Witkop, B., and Udenfriend, S.: Hydroxylation-induced migration: The NIH shift, Science 157:1524, 1967.
153. Gursey, D., Vester, J. W., and Olson, R. E.: Effect of ethanol administration upon serotonin and norepinephrine levels in rabbit brain, J. Clin. Invest. 38:1008, 1959.

154. Gyermek, L.: 5-Hydroxytryptamine antagonists, Pharmacol. Rev. 13: 399, 1961.
155. ———: Drugs which antagonize 5-hydroxytryptamine and related indole-alkylamines. From "5-Hydroxytryptamine and related indolealkylamines." Subed. V. Erspamer. 19. Handbook of Experimental Pharmacology, Springer-Verlag, New York, 1966.
156. Haber, B., and Kamano, A.: Subcellular distribution of serotonin in the developing rat brain, Nature, London 209:404, 1966.
157. Haddox, C. H., Jr., and Saslaw, M. S.: Urinary 5-methoxytryptamine in patients with rheumatic fever, J. Clin. Invest. 42:435, 1963.
158. Halberg, F., Anderson, J. A., Ertel, R., and Berendes, H.: Circadian rhythm in serum 5-hydroxytryptamine of healthy men and male patients with mental retardation, Internat. J. Neuropsych., July-Aug., 1967, p. 379.
159. Hallén, A.: Fibrosis in the carcinoid syndrome, Lancet 1:746, 1964.
160. Halpern, A., Kuhn, P. H., Shaftel, H. E., Samuels, S. S., Shaftel, N., Selman, D., and Birch, H. G.: Raynaud's disease, Raynaud's phenomenon and serotonin, Angiology 11:151, 1960.
161. Hamlin, K. E., and Fischer, F. E.: The synthesis of 5-hydroxytryptamine, J. Am. Chem. Soc. 73:5007, 1951.
162. Handschumacher, R. E., and Vane, J. R.: The relationship between the penetration of tryptamine and 5-hydroxytryptamine into smooth muscle and the associated contraction, Brit. J. Pharmacol. 29:105, 1967.
163. Hardisty, R. M., and Stacey, R. S.: 5-Hydroxytryptamine in normal human platelets, J. Physiol. 130:711, 1955.
164. Hare, M. L. C.: Tyramine oxidase. I. A new enzyme system in liver, Biochem. J. 22:968, 1928.
165. Haverback, B. J.: Serotonin and the gastrointestinal tract, Clin. Res. 6:57, 1958.
166. Heller, A., Harvey, J. A., and Moore, R. Y.: A demonstration of a fall in brain serotonin following central nervous system lesions in the rat, Biochem. Pharmacol. 11:859, 1962.
167. ———, and Moore, R. Y.: Effect of central nervous system lesions on brain monoamines in the rat, J. Pharmacol. & Exper. Therap. 150:1, 1965.
168. ———, and Moore, R. Y.: Control of Brain Serotonin and Norepinephrine by Specific Neural Systems, in *Advances in Pharmacology*, Academic Press, New York, 1968, Vol. 6A, p. 191.
169. Highton, T. C., and Garrett, M. H.: Some effects of serotonin and related compounds on human collagen, Lancet 1:1234, 1963.
170. Hillarp, N. A., Fuxe, K., and Dahlström, A.: Demonstration and mapping of central neurons containing dopamine, noradrenaline and 5-hydroxytryptamine and their reactions to psychopharmaca, Pharmacol. Rev. 18:727, 1966.
171. Holzbauer, M., and Vogt, M.: Depression by reserpine of the noradrenaline concentration in the hypothalamus of the cat, J. Neurochem. 1:8, 1956–57.
172. Horton, E. W.: An increase in butanol-extractable 5-hydroxytryptamine in venous blood during reactive hyperaemia, J. Physiol. 170:101, 1964.
173. Humphrey, J. H., and Jaques, R.: The release of histamine and 5-hydroxytryptamine (serotonin) from platelets by antigen-antibody reaction (in vitro), J. Physiol. 128:9, 1955.

174. ———, and Toh, C. C.: Absorption of serotonin (5-hydroxytryptamine) and histamine by dog platelets, J. Physiol. 124:300, 1954.

175. Isbell, H., Winer, E. J., and Logan, C. R.: Relationship of psychotomimetic to antiserotonin potencies of congeners of lysergic acid diethylamide (LSD-25), Psychopharmacol. 1:20, 1959.

176. Isler, P., and Hedinger, C.: Metastasierendes Dünndarmcarcinoid mit schwerem, vorwiegend das rechte Herz betreffenden Klappenfehlen und Pulmonalstenose-ein eigenartiger Symptomenkomplex? Schweiz. med. Wchnschr. 83:5, 1953.

177. Jequier, E.: Effect of serotonin on synaptic transmission in the isolated sympathetic cervical ganglion of the rat, Helvet. physiol. et pharmacol. acta 23:163, 1965.

178. ———, Lovenberg, W., and Sjoerdsma, A.: Tryptophan hydroxylase inhibition: The mechanism by which p-chlorophenylamine depletes rat brain serotonin, Molec. Pharmacol. 3:274, 1967.

179. Johansson, B., and Roos, B.-E.: 5-Hydroxyindoleacetic and homovanillic acid levels in the cerebrospinal fluid of healthy volunteers and patients with Parkinson's syndrome, Life Sc. 6:1449, 1967.

180. Johnson, L. P., Sloop, R. D., and Jesseph, J. E.: Treatment of "dumping" with serotonin antagonists. Preliminary report, J.A.M.A. 180:493, 1962.

181. Johnson, S. A., Mouts, R. W., Rebreck, J. W., and Horn, R. C.: *Blood Platelets,* Little, Brown & Co., Boston, 1960.

182. Jouvet, M.: The states of sleep, Scient. Am. 216:62, 1967.

183. Kaneko, Y., McCubbin, J. W., and Page, I. H.: Mechanism by which serotonin, norepinephrine and reserpine cause central vasomotor inhibition, Circulation Res. 8:1228, 1960.

184. Karki, N., Kuntzman, R., and Brodie, B. B.: Storage, synthesis and metabolism of monoamines in the developing brain, J. Neurochem. 9:53, 1962.

185. Koe, B. K., and Weissman, A.: p-Chlorophenylalanine: A specific depletor of brain serotonin, J. Pharmacol. & Exper. Therap. 154:499, 1966.

186. Koella, W. P., Smythies, J. R., Levy, C. K., and Czicman, J. S.: Modulatory influence on cerebral cortical optic response from the carotid sinus area, Am. J. Physiol. 199:381, 1960.

187. Krapcho, J., Rubin, B., Dunges, A. M., Spitzmiller, E. R., Turk, C. F., Williams, J., Craver, B. N., and Freid, J.: 2'- (3-Dimethylaminopropylthio) cinnamanilide and related compounds—a new class of potent and relatively specific serotonin inhibitors, J. Med. Chem. 6:219, 1963.

188. ———, and Turk, C. F.: Serotonin inhibitors. III. Compounds related to 2'- (3-dimethylaminopropylthio) cinnamanilide, J. Med. Chem. 9:809, 1966.

189. Kveder, S., Iskrić, S., and Keglević, D.: 5-Hydroxytryptophol: A metabolite of 5-hydroxytryptamine in rats, Biochem. J. 85:447, 1962.

190. Kwaan, H. C., Lo, R., and McFadzean, A. J. S.: The production of plasma fibrinolytic activity in vivo by serotonin (5-hydroxytryptamine) creatinine sulphate, Clin. Sc. 16:255, 1957.

191. Lance, J. W., Anthony, M., and Gonski, A.: Serotonin, the carotid body, and cranial vessels in migraine, Arch. Neurol. 16:553, 1967.

192. ———, Anthony, M., and Hinterberger, H.: The control of cranial arteries by humoral mechanisms and its relation to the migraine syndrome, Headache 7:93, 1967.

193. Landis, E. M., Wood, J. E., and Guerrant, J. L.: Effect of heparin on the vasoconstrictor action of shed blood tested by perfusion of the rabbit's ear, Am. J. Physiol. 139:26, 1943.

194. Lembeck, F.: 5-Hydroxytryptamine in a carcinoid tumor, Nature, London 172:910, 1953.

195. Lerner, A. B., Case, J. D., Takahashi, Y., Lee, T. H., and Mori, W.: Isolation of melatonin, the pineal gland factor that lightens melanocytes, J. Am. Chem. Soc. 80:2587, 1958.

196. Levine, R. A., Pesch, L. A., Klatskin, G., and Giarman, N. J.: Effect of serotonin on glycogen metabolism in isolated rat liver, J. Clin. Invest. 43:797, 1964.

197. Lovenberg, W., Jequier, E., and Sjoerdsma, A.: Tryptophan hydroxylation: Measurement in pineal gland, brain stem and carcinoid tumor, Science 155:217, 1967.

198. MacDonald, R. A.: Pathogenesis of lesions induced by serotonin, Am. J. Path. 35:297, 1959.

199. McCaman, R. E., McCaman, M. W., Hunt, J. M., and Smith, M. C.: Microdetermination of monoamine oxidase and 5-hydroxytryptophan decarboxylase activities in nervous tissues, J. Neurochem. 12:15, 1965.

200. McCubbin, J. W., Green, J. H., Salmoiraghi, G. C., and Page, I. H.: The chemoreceptor stimulant action of serotonin in dogs, J. Pharmacol. & Exper. Therap. 116:191, 1956.

201. ————, Kaneko, Y., and Page, I. H.: Ability of serotonin and norepinephrine to mimic the central effects of reserpine on vasomotor activity, Circulation Res. 8:849, 1960.

202. ————, Kaneko, Y., and Page, I. H.: Inhibition of neurogenic vasoconstriction by serotonin, Circulation Res. 11:74, 1962.

203. McGeer, E. G., and McGeer, P. L.: Circadian rhythm in pineal tyrosine hydroxylase, Science 153:73, 1966.

204. McIsaac, W. M., and Page, I. H.: The metabolism of serotonin (5-hydroxytryptamine), J. Biol. Chem. 234:858, 1959.

205. McKean, C. M., Schanberg, S. M., and Giarman, N. J.: Aminoacidemias: Effects on maze performance and cerebral serotonin, Science 157:213, 1967.

206. McKinney, B., and Crawford, M. A.: Fibrosis in guinea pig hearts produced by plantain diet, Lancet 2:880, 1965.

207. Majno, G., Gilmore, V., and Leventhal, M.: On the mechanism of vascular leakage caused by histamine-type mediators, Circulation Res. 21: 833, 1967.

208. Mansour, T. E.: The effect of serotonin and related compounds on the carbohydrate metabolism of the liver fluke Fasciola hepatica, J. Pharmacol. & Exper. Therap. 126:212, 1959.

209. ————: The effect of serotonin on glycolysis in homogenates from the liver fluke Fasciola hepatica, J. Pharmacol. & Exper. Therap. 135:94, 1962.

210. ————: Effect of hormones on carbohydrate metabolism of invertebrates, Fed. Proc. 26:1179, 1967.

211. ————, and Lago, A. D.: Biochemical effects of serotonin on Fasciola hepatica, J. Pharmacol. & Exper. Therap. 122:48A, 1958.

212. ————, and Mansour, J. M.: Effect of serotonin and adenosine 3',5'-phosphate on phosphofructokinase from the liver fluke, Fasciola hepatica, J. Biol. Chem. 237:629, 1962.

213. ———, Sutherland, E. W., Rall, T. W., and Bueding, E.: The effect of serotonin (5-hydroxytryptamine) on the formation of adenosine 3',5'-phosphate by tissue particles from the liver fluke, Fasciola hepatica, J. Biol. Chem. 235:466, 1960.

214. Mantegazzini, P.: Pharmacological actions of indolealkylamines and precursor amino acids on the central nervous system, Handb. exper. Pharmacol. 19:424, Springer, Berlin, 1966.

215. Markwardt, F., and Barthel, W.: Untersuchungen über die Freisetzung von Serotonin aus Blutplättchen durch Thrombin, Arch. exper. Path. u. Pharmakol. 249:176, 1964.

216. Marley, P. B., Robson, J. M., and Sullivan, F. M.: Embryotoxic and teratogenic action of 5-hydroxytryptamine: Mechanism of action in the rat, Brit. J. Pharmacol. 31:494, 1967.

217. Marrazzi, A. S., and Hart, E. R.: The possible role of inhibition at adrenergic synapses in the mechanism of hallucinogenic and related drug actions, J. Nerv. & Ment. Dis. 122:435, 1955.

218. Mason, D. T., and Melmon, K. L.: Abnormal forearm vascular responses in the carcinoid syndrome, the role of kinins and kinin-generating system, J. Clin. Invest. 45:1685, 1966.

219. Mattingly, T. W.: Functioning carcinoid tumor—a new clinical entity. Review of the clinical features of the non-functioning and the functioning carcinoid, including a review of thirty-eight cases from the literature, Med. Ann. D. C. 25:239, 304, 1956.

220. Maynard, D. M., and Welsh, J.: Neurohumors of the pericardial organs of Brachyuran Crustacea, J. Physiol. 149:215, 1959.

221. Miller, J., and Fishman, A.: A serotonin antagonist in the treatment of allergic and allied disorders, Ann. Allergy 19:164, 1961.

222. Milne, W. L., and Cohn, S. H.: Role of serotonin in blood coagulation, Am. J. Physiol. 189:470, 1957.

223. Moran, N. C., Uvnäs, B., and Westerholm, B.: Release of 5-hydroxytryptamine and histamine from rat mast cells, Acta physiol. scandinav. 56:26, 1962.

224. ———, and Westerholm, B.: The influence of reserpine on 5-hydroxytryptamine and histamine content of rat mast cells and of some rat tissues, Acta physiol. scandinav. 58:20, 1963.

224a. Myers, R. D., and Veale, W. L.: Alcohol preference in the rat: Reduction following depletion of brain serotonin, Science 160:1469, 1968.

225. Oates, J. A., Melmon, K., Sjoerdsma, A., Gillespie, L., and Mason, D. T.: Release of a kinin peptide in the carcinoid syndrome, Lancet 1:514, 1964.

226. ———, and Sjoerdsma, A.: A unique syndrome associated with secretion of 5-hydroxytryptophan by metastatic gastric carcinoids, Am. J. Med. 32:333, 1962.

227. Oberndorfer, S.: Karzinoide Tumoren das Dünndarms, Frankfurt Ztschr. Path. 1:426, 1907.

228. Offermier, J., and Ariëns, E. J.: Serotonin. II. Structural variation and action, Arch. internat. pharmacodyn. 164:216, 1966.

229. Ojo, G. O., and Parratt, J. R.: Urinary excretion of 5-hydroxyindoleacetic acid in Nigerians with endomyocardial fibrosis, Lancet 1:854, 1966.

230. Olson, R. E., Gursey, D., and Vester, J. W.: Evidence for a defect in tryptophan metabolism in chronic alcoholism, New England J. Med. 263:1169, 1960.

231. Owman, C.: Sympathetic nerves probably storing two types of monoamines in the rat pineal gland, Internat. J. Neuropharmacol. 3:105, 1964.
232. Paasonen, M. K.: Mechanism of chlorpromazine action in releasing 5-hydroxytryptamine from blood platelets in vitro, Arch. Exper. Path. 248: 223, 1964.
233. ———, MacLean, P. D., and Giarman, N. J.: 5-Hydroxytryptamine (serotonin, enteramine) content of structures of the limbic system, J. Neurochem. 1:326, 1957.
234. Page, E. W., and Glendening, M. B.: Production of renal cortical necrosis with serotonin (5-hydroxytryptamine), Obst. & Gynec. 5:781, 1955.
235. Page, I. H.: *Chemistry of the Brain,* Charles C Thomas, Publisher, Springfield, Ill., 1937.
236. ———: Nature and treatment of oligemic shock, Am. Heart J. 38:161, 1949.
237. ———: Pathogenesis of arterial hypertension, J.A.M.A. 140:451, 1949.
238. ———: The vascular action of natural serotonin, 5- and 7-hydroxytyramine and tryptamine, J. Pharmacol & Exper. Therap. 105:58, 1952.
239. ———: Serotonin (5-hydroxytryptamine), Physiol. Rev. 34:563, 1954.
240. ———: Serotonin (5-hydroxytryptamine) the last four years, Physiol. Rev. 38:277, 1958.
241. ———, Corcoran, A. C., Udenfriend, S., Sjoerdsma, A., and Weissbach, H.: Argentaffinoma as endocrine tumor, Lancet 1:198, 1955.
242. ———, and McCubbin, J. W.: "Serotonin" or "tenure for the pharmacologist," Circulation 14:161, 1956.
243. ———, and McCubbin, J. W.: The variable arterial pressure response to serotonin in laboratory animals and man, Circulation Res. 1:354, 1953.
244. ———, and McCubbin, J. W.: Arterial pressure response to infused serotonin in normotensive dogs, cats, hypertensive dogs and man, Am. J. Physiol. 184:265, 1956.
245. Palaić, D., Page, I. H., and Khairallah, P. A.: Uptake and metabolism of (^{14}C) serotonin in rat brain, J. Neurochem. 14:63, 1967.
246. ———, and Supek, Z.: Drug-induced changes of the metabolism of 5-hydroxytryptamine in the brain of x-ray-treated rats, J. Neurochem. 12: 329, 1965.
247. Pare, C. M. B., Sandler, M., and Stacey, R. S.: 5-Hydroxytryptamine deficiency in phenylketonuria, Lancet 1:551, 1957.
248. ———, Sandler, M., and Stacey, R. S.: Decreased 5-hydroxytryptophan decarboxylase activity in phenylketonuria, Lancet 2:1099, 1958.
249. Parratt, J. R., and West, G. B.: 5-Hydroxytryptamine and tissue mast cells, J. Physiol. 137:169, 1957.
250. Pax, R. A., and Sanborn, R. C.: Cardioregulation in Limulus. III. Inhibition by 5-hydroxytryptamine and antagonism by bromolysergic acid diethylamide and picrotoxin, Biol. Bull. 132:392, 1967.
251. Pernow, B., and Waldenström, J.: Determination of 5-hydroxytryptamine, 5-hydroxyindoleacetic acid and histamine in thirty-three cases of carcinoid tumor (argentaffinoma), Am. J. Med. 23:16, 1957.
252. Perry, T. L., Hansen, S., Tischler, B., and Hestrin, M.: Defective 5-hydroxylation of tryptophan in phenylketonuria, Proc. Soc. Exper. Biol. & Med. 115:118, 1964.
253. Pletscher, A.: Basic aspects of psychotropic drug action, Am. J. Ment. Deficiency 67:238, 1962.

254. ———, Burkard, W. P., Bruderer, H., and Gey, K. F.: Decrease of cerebral 5-hydroxytryptamine and 5-hydroxyindoleacetic acid by an aryl alkyl amine, Life Sc. 2:828, 1963.

255. ———, Shore, P. A., and Brodie, B. B.: Serotonin release as a possible mechanism of reserpine action, Science 122:374, 1955.

256. Pollin, W., Cardon, P. V., and Kety, S. S.: Effects of amino acid feedings in schizophrenic patients treated with iproniazid, Science 133:104, 1961.

257. Poulson, E., Robson, J. M., and Sullivan, F. M.: Teratogenic effect of 5-hydroxytryptamine in mice, Science 141:717, 1963.

258. Prusoff, W. H.: The distribution of 5-hydroxytryptamine and adenosine triphosphate in cytoplasmic particles of the dog's small intestine, Brit. J. Pharmacol. 15:520, 1960.

259. Pscheidt, G. R., Morpurgo, C., and Himwich, H. E.: Studies on Norepinephrine and 5-Hydroxytryptamine in Various Species, in *Comparative Neurochemistry*, Proc. 5th Internat. Neurochem. Symp., Pergamon Press, New York, 1964.

260. Quay, W. B.: Circadian rhythm in rat pineal serotonin and its modifications by estrous cycle and photoperiod, Gen. Comp. Endocrinol. 3: 473, 1963.

261. ———: Circadian and estrous rhythms in pineal melatonin and 5-hydroxyindole-3-acetic acid, Proc. Soc. Exper. Biol. & Med. 115:710, 1964.

262. ———: Indole derivatives of pineal and related neural and retinal tissue, Pharmacol. Rev. 17:321, 1965.

263. ———: Twenty-four hour rhythms in cerebral and brain-stem contents of 5-hydroxytryptamine in a turtle. Pseudemys scripta elegans, Compt. Biochem. Physiol. 20:217, 1967.

264. ———, and Halevy, A.: Experimental modification of the rat pineal's content of serotonin and related indole amines. Physiol. Zoöl. 35:1, 1962.

265. ———, and Wilhoft, D. C.: Comparative and regional differences in serotonin content of reptilian brains, J. Neurochem. 11:805, 1964.

266. Rapport, M. M., Green, A. A., and Page, I. H.: Partial purification of the vasoconstrictor in beef serum, J. Biol. Chem. 174:735, 1948.

267. ———, Green, A. A., and Page, I. H.: Crystalline serotonin, Science 108: 329, 1948.

268. ———, Green, A. A., and Page, I. H.: Serum vasoconstrictor (serotonin). III. Chemical inactivation, J. Biol. Chem. 176:1237, 1948.

269. ———, Green, A. A., and Page, I. H.: Serum vasoconstrictor (serotonin). IV. Isolation and characterization, J. Biol. Chem. 176:1243, 1948.

270. Reddy, D. V., Adams, F. H., and Baird, C.: Teratogenic effects of serotonin, J. Pediat. 63:394, 1963.

271. Reichle, F. A., Brigham, M. P., and Rosemond, G. P.: Serotonin and the dumping syndrome, J.A.M.A. 199:914, 1967.

272. Reid, G: Circulatory effects of 5-hydroxytryptamine, J. Physiol. 118: 435, 1952.

273. Renson, J., Daly, J., Weissbach, H., Witkop, B., and Udenfriend, S.: Enzymatic conversion of 5-tritiotryptophan to 4-tritio-5-hydroxytryptophan, Biochem. Res. Comm. et Biophys. Res. Comm. 25:504, 1966.

274. ———, Weissbach, H., and Udenfriend, S.: Hydroxylation of tryptophan by phenylalanine hydroxylase, J. Biol. Chem. 237:2261, 1962.

275. Riley, J. F., and Shepherd, D. M.: Mast cells, tryptophan and 5-hydroxytryptamine in precancerous mouse skin, Experientia 21:498, 1965.

276. Ritzén, M., Hammarström, L., and Ullberg, S.: Autoradiographic distribution of 5-hydroxytryptamine and 5-hydroxytryptophan in the mouse, Biochem. Pharmacol. 14:313, 1965.

277. Robertson, J. I. S., and Andrews, T. M.: Free serotonin in human plasma—quantitative and qualitative estimation, Lancet 1:578, 1961.

278. Robertson, J. I. S., Peart, W. S., and Andrews, T. M.: The mechanism of facial flushes in the carcinoid syndrome, Quart. J. Med. 31:103, 1962.

279. Robinson, J. D., Anderson, J. H., and Green, J. P.: The uptake of 5-hydroxytryptamine and histamine by particulate fractions of brain, J. Pharmacol. & Exper. Therap. 147:236, 1965.

280. Roddie, I. C., Shepherd, J. T., and Whelan, R. F.: The action of 5-hydroxytryptamine on blood vessels of the human hand and forearm, Brit. J. Pharmacol. 10:445, 1955.

281. Rosenberg, J. C., Lillehei, R. C., Longerbeam, J., and Zimmerman, B.: Studies on hemorrhagic and endotoxin shock in relation to vasomotor changes and endogenous circulating epinephrine, norepinephrine and serotonin, Ann. Surg. 154:611, 1961.

282. Rosner, F., Ong, B. H., Paine, R. S., and Mahanand, D.: Blood-serotonin activity in trisomic and translocation Down's syndrome, Lancet 1:1191, 1965.

283. Rowley, D. A., and Benditt, E. P.: 5-Hydroxytryptamine and histamine as mediators of the vascular injury produced by agents which damage mast cells in rats, J. Exper. Med. 103:399, 1956.

284. Rudolph, A. M., and Paul, M. H.: Pulmonary and systemic vascular response to continuous infusion of 5-hydroxytryptamine (serotonin) in the dog, Am. J. Physiol. 189:263, 1957.

285. Sandler, M., Scheuer, P. J., and Watt, P. J.: 5-hydroxytryptophan-secreting bronchial carcinoid tumor, Lancet 2:1067, 1961.

286. ———, and Snow, P. D. J.: An atypical carcinoid tumor secreting 5-hydroxytryptophan, Lancet 1:137, 1958.

287. Sanyal, R. K., and West, G. B.: The relationship of histamine and 5-hydroxytryptamine to anaphylactic shock in different species, J. Physiol. 144:525, 1958.

288. ———, and West, G. B.: The role of histamine and 5-hydroxytryptamine (5-HT) in injury. Internat. Arch. Allergy 26:362, 1965.

289. Sauer, W. G., Dearing, W. H., and Flock, E. V.: Diagnosis and clinical management of functioning carcinoids, J.A.M.A. 168:139, 1958.

290. Schain, R. J., and Freedman, D. X.: Studies on 5-hydroxyindole metabolism in autistic and other mentally retarded children, J. Pediat. 58:315, 1961.

291. Schanberg, S. M.: A study of the transport of 5-hydroxytryptophan and 5-hydroxytryptamine, J. Pharmacol. & Exper. Therap. 139:191, 1963.

292. Scherbel, A. L., and Harrison, J. W.: Exaggerated reactivity to serotonin in patients with rheumatoid arthritis and related diseases, Circulation 18:777, 1958.

293. ———, and Harrison, J. W.: Response to serotonin and its antagonists in patients with rheumatoid arthritis and related diseases, Angiology 10:29, 1959.

294. Schlesinger, K., Boggan, W., and Freedman, D. X.: Genetics of audiogenic seizures: I. Relation to brain serotonin and norepinephrine in mice, Life Sc. 4:2345, 1965.

295. Schneckloth, R. E., Page, I. H., Del Greco, F., and Corcoran, A. C.: Effects of serotonin antagonists in normal subjects and patients with carcinoid tumors, Circulation 16:523, 1957.

296. Selye, H.: Studies on adaptation, Endocrinology 21:169, 1937.

297. ———: Experimental production of endomyocardial fibrosis, Lancet 1: 1351, 1958.

298. ———: Anaphylactoid edema; 1937-1967. Perspectives Biol. Med. 11:247, 1968.

299. ———, Tuckweber, B., and Rohan, P.: Thromboses in large veins and pulmonary embolisms induced by catecholamines or serotonin, Nature, London 208:900, 1965.

300. Sicuteri, F.: Prophylactic and therapeutic properties of 1-methyl-lysergic acid butanolamide in migraine, Internat. Arch. Allergy 15:300, 1959.

301. Sigg, E. B.: Pharmacological studies with trofanil, Canad. Psychiat. A. J. 4:75, 1959.

302. Shaper, A. G.: Plantain diets, serotonin, and endomyocardial fibrosis, Am. Heart J. 73:432, 1967.

303. Sharpey-Schafer, E. P., and Ginsberg, J.: Humoral agents and venous tone: Effects of catecholamines, 5-hydroxytryptamine, histamine and nitrites, Lancet 2:1337, 1962.

304. Shein, H. M., Wurtman, R. J., and Axelrod, J.: Synthesis of serotonin by pineal glands of the rat in organ culture, Nature, London 213:730, 1967.

305. Sirek, A., Geerling, E., and Sirek, O. V.: Serotonin as the hyperglycemic substance released by growth hormone, Am. J. Physiol. 211:1018, 1966.

306. Sjoerdsma, A.: Serotonin, New England J. Med. 261:181, 231, 1959.

307. ———, and Melmon, K. L.: The carcinoid spectrum, Gastroenterology 47:104, 1964.

308. ———, Waalkes, T. P., and Weissbach, H.: Serotonin and histamine in mast cells, Science 125:1202, 1957.

309. ———, Weissbach, H., and Udenfriend, S.: A clinical, physiologic and biochemical study of patients with malignant carcinoid (argentaffinoma), Am. J. Med. 20:520, 1956.

310. Smith, B., and Prockop, D. J.: Central-nervous-system effects of ingestion of L-tryptophan by normal subjects, New England J. Med. 267:1338, 1962.

311. Snyder, S. H., Axelrod, J., Wurtman, R. J., and Fisher, J. E.: Control of 5-hydroxytryptophan decarboxylase activity in the rat pineal gland by sympathetic nerves, J. Pharmacol. & Exper. Therap. 147:371, 1965.

312. Snyder, S. H., Axelrod, J., and Zweig, M.: A sensitive and specific fluorescence assay for tissue serotonin, Biochem. Pharmacol. 14:831, 1965.

313. ———, Zweig, M., and Axelrod, J.: Control of the circadian rhythm in serotonin content of the rat pineal gland, Life Sc. 3:1175, 1964.

314. Sollero, L.: Serotonina e substancias antitriptaminicas: Revisao—contribuicao experimental, Univ. do Brasil Inst. de Biofisica, Rio de Janeiro, 1963.

315. Spaet, T. H., and Zucker, M. B.: Mechanism of platelet plug formation and role of adenosine diphosphate, Am. J. Physiol. 206:1267, 1964.

316. Sparrow, E. M., and Wilhelm, D. L.: Species differences in susceptibility to capillary permeability factors: Histamine, 5-hydroxytryptamine and compound 48/80, J. Physiol. 137:51, 1957.

317. Spector, S., Sjoerdsma, A., and Udenfriend, S.: Blockade of endogenous norepinephrine synthesis by alpha-methyl-tyrosine, an inhibitor of tyrosine hydroxylase, J. Pharmacol. & Exper. Therap. 147:86, 1965.

318. ———, and Willoughby, D. A.: 5-Hydroxytryptamine in acute inflammation, Nature, London 179:318, 1957.

319. Stacey, R. S.: Malignant carcinoid tumors, Proc. Roy. Soc. Med. 50:40, 1957.

320. Stark, P., Boyd, E. S., and Fuller, R. W.: A possible role of serotonin in hypothalamic self-stimulation in dogs, J. Pharmacol. & Exper. Therap. 146:147, 1964.

321. Starling, E. H., and Verney, E. B.: The secretion of urine as studied on the isolated kidney, Proc. Roy. Soc. B. 97:321, 1925.

322. Stone, C. A., Wenger, H. C., Ludden, C. T., Stavorski, J. M., and Ross, C. A.: Antiserotonin—antihistaminic properties of cyproheptadine, J. Pharmacol. & Exper. Therap. 131:73, 1961.

323. ———, and Mansour, T. E.: Phosphofructokinase from liver fluke Fasciola hepatica. I. Activation by adenosine 3′,5′-phosphate and by serotonin, Mol. Pharmacol. 3:161, 1967.

324. Sudak, H. S., and Maas, J. W.: Central nervous system serotonin and norepinephrine localization in emotional and non-emotional strains of mice, Nature, London 203:1254, 1964.

325. Sutherland, E. W., Robison, A. G., and Butcher, R. W.: Some aspects of the biological role of adenosine 3′,5′-monophosphate (cyclic AMP), Circulation 38:279, 1968.

326. Swank, R. L., Fellman, J. H., and Hissen, W. W.: Aggregation of blood cells by 5-hydroxytryptamine (serotonin), Circulation Res. 13:392, 1963.

327. Swank, R. L., Hissen, W., and Fellman, J. H.: 5-Hydroxytryptamine (serotonin) in acute hypotensive shock, Am. J. Physiol. 207:215, 1964.

328. Tanimukai, H., Ginther, B., Spaide, J., Buenos, J. E., and Himwich, H. E.: Occurrence of bufotenin (5-hydroxy-N,N-dimethyltryptamine) in urine of schizophrenic patients, Life Sc. 6:1697, 1967.

329. Thomas, D. P., and Vane, J. R.: 5-Hydroxytryptamine in the circulation of the dog, Nature, London 216:335, 1967.

330. Thorson, A., Biörck, G., Bjorkman, G., and Waldenström, J.: Malignant carcinoid of the small intestine with metastasis to the liver, valvular disease of the right side of the heart (pulmonary stenosis and tricuspid regurgitation without septal defect), peripheral vasomotor symptoms, bronchoconstriction and an unusual type of cyanosis. A clinical and pathologic syndrome, Am. Heart J. 47:795, 1954.

331. Tobe, T., Kimura, C., and Fujiwara, M.: Role of 5-hydroxytryptamine in dumping syndrome after gastrectomy, Ann. Surg. 165:382, 1967.

332. Tochino, Y., and Schanker, L. S.: Transport of serotonin and norepinephrine by the rabbit choroid plexus in vitro, Biochem. Pharmacol. 14:1557, 1965.

333. Trendelenburg, U.: The action of 5-hydroxytryptamine on the nictitating membrane and on the superior cervical ganglion of the cat, Brit. J. Pharmacol. 11:74, 1956.

334. Tu, J., and Zellweger, H.: Blood-serotonin deficiency in Down's syndrome, Lancet 2:715, 1965.

335. Twarog, B. M.: Responses of a molluscan smooth muscle to acetylcholine and 5-hydroxytryptamine, J. Cell. & Comp. Physiol. 44:141, 1954.

336. ———, and Page, I. H.: Serotonin content of some mammalian tissues and urine and a method for its determination, Am. J. Physiol. 175:157, 1953.

337. Udenfriend, S., Bogdanski, D. F., and Weissbach, H.: Increase in tissue serotonin by administration of its precursor, 5-hydroxytryptophan, Fed. Proc. 15:493, 1956.

338. ———, Clark, C. T., and Titus, E.: 5-Hydroxytryptophan decarboxylase: A new route of metabolism of tryptophan, J. Am. Chem. Soc. 75:501, 1953.

339. ———, Titus, E., and Weissbach, H.: The identification of 5-hydroxyindoleacetic acid in normal urine and a new method of its assay, J. Biol. Chem. 125:1202, 1957.

340. ———, Weissbach, H., and Bogdanski, D. F.: Increase in tissue serotonin following administration of its precursor 5-hydroxytryptophan, J. Biol. Chem. 224:803, 1957.

341. Uuspää, V. J.: The 5-hydroxytryptamine content of the brain and some other organs of the hedgehog (Erinaceus europaeus) during activity and hibernation, Experientia 19:156, 1963.

342. Uvnäs, B.: Release processes in mast cells and their activation by injury, Ann. New York Acad. Sc. 116:880, 1964.

343. Vanable, J. W., Jr.: A ninhydrin reaction giving a sensitive quantitative fluorescence assay for 5-hydroxytryptamine, Ann. Biochem. 6:393, 1963.

344. Vane, J. R.: The relative activities of some tryptamine analogues on the isolated rat stomach strip preparation, Brit. J. Pharmacol. 14:87, 1959.

345. ———: The use of isolated organs for detecting active substances in the circulating blood, Brit. J. Pharmacol. 23:360, 1964.

346. Vyden, J. K., Gold, H., Bernstein, H., and Corday, E.: Effect of 5-hydroxytryptamine (serotonin) on regional circulations, Circulation, supp. II. 36:II-258, 1967.

347. Waalkes, T. P., Weissbach, H., Bozicevich, J., and Udenfriend, S.: Serotonin and histamine release during anaphylaxis in the rabbit, J. Clin. Invest. 36:1115, 1957.

348. Waugh, D., and Pearl, M. J.: Serotonin-induced acute nephrosis and renal cortical necrosis in rats; a morphologic study with pregnancy correlations, Am. J. Path. 36:431, 1960.

349. Weber, L. J., and Horita, A.: A study of 5-hydroxytryptamine formation from L-tryptophan in the brain and other tissues, Biochem. Pharmacol. 14:1141, 1965.

350. Weight, F. F., and Salmoiraghi, G. C.: Responses of spinal cord interneurons to acetylcholine, norepinephrine and serotonin administered by microelectrophoresis, J. Pharmacol. & Exper. Therap. 153:420, 1966.

351. Weissbach, H., Waalkes, T. P., and Udenfriend, S.: Presence of serotonin in lung and its implication in anaphylactic reaction, Science 125:235, 1957.

352. Welsh, J. H., and Moorhead, M.: The quantitative distribution of 5-hydroxytryptamine in the invertebrates, especially in their nervous systems, J. Neurochem. 6:146, 1960.

353. West, G. B.: 5-Hydroxytryptamine, tissue mast cells and skin oedema, Internat. Arch. Allergy 10:257, 1957.

354. Whelan, R. F.: *Control of the Peripheral Circulation in Man,* Charles C Thomas, Publisher, Springfield, Ill., 1967.

355. Whittaker, V. P.: The subcellular localization of transmitter substances in the central nervous system, Biochem. Pharmacol. 5:392, 1961.
356. Woolley, D. W.: Highly potent antimetabolites of serotonin with little serotonin-like action, Biochem. Pharmacol. 3:51, 1959.
357. Wulfsohn, N. L., and Politzer, W. N.: 5-Hydroxytryptamine in dyspnea and asthma, S. African J. Med. Sc. 27:67, 1962.
358. Wurtman, R. J., Axelrod, J., Chu, E. W., Heller, A., and Moore, R. Y.: Medial forebrain bundle lesions: Blockade of effects of light on rat gonads and pineal, Endocrinology 81:509, 1967.
359. ———, Axelrod, J., and Fischer, J. E.: Melatonin synthesis in the pineal gland: Effect of light mediated by the sympathetic nervous system, Science 143:1328, 1964.
360. ———, and Kammer, H.: Melatonin synthesis by an ectopic pinealoma, New England J. Med. 274:1233, 1966.
361. Wurzel, M.: Serotonin receptor in rabbit artery, Am. J. Physiol. 211: 1424, 1966.
362. Yuwiler, A., Geller, E., and Slater, G. G.: On the mechanism of the brain serotonin depletion in experimental phenylketonuria, J. Biol. Chem. 240:1170, 1965.
363. Zeitlin, I. J., and Smith, A. N.: 5-Hydroxyindoles and kinins in the carcinoid and dumping syndromes, Lancet 2:986, 1966.
364. Zucker, M. B., and Borrelli, J.: Absorption of serotonin (5-hydroxytryptamine) by canine and human platelets, Am. J. Physiol. 186:105, 1956.
365. Zucker, M. B., Hellman, L., and Zumoff, B.: Rapid disappearance of C^{14}-labeled serotonin from platelets in patients with carcinoid syndrome, J. Lab. & Clin. Med. 63:137, 1964.

Index

137

Bradykinin: production of, 107
Brain
  blood-brain barrier, 59
  "chemistry," 55
  5-hydroxylation of tryptophan in,
    25-27
  serotonin antagonism in, 36
  serotonin of, 16, 55-73
    circadian rhythm and, 70-72
    content changes, 59-60
    content, tryptophan in diet and,
      59
    depletion, 36
    distribution 55-58
    effects on neural function, 60-62
    serotonin as transmitter, 62-67
    serotonin as transmitter, mech-
      anisms, 68-70
Breakdown: of serotonin, 38-40
Breast: hypertrophy, 97
Bromolysergic acid diethylamide, 65
Bronchial adenoma, 107-108
Bufotenine, 81
  schizophrenia and, 82

C

Carbohydrate metabolism: and sero-
    tonin, 40-43
Carcinoids
  flush of, 106
    chlorpromazine and, 108
  serotonin and, 104-109
  syndrome, 32
  tumors, and chlorpromazine, 89
Catecholamines, 58
  chlorpromazine and, 76
  synthesis and degradation of, 26
Cells
  enterochromaffin, and seritonin, 16
  reticuloendothelial, and serotonin
    uptake, 29
  serotonergic neuron cell bodies, 56
Cerebellum: serotonin in, 56
Cerebrum
  cortex, evoked optic response to
    serotonin,
  metabolism, 55
Chemical: distribution of, 15-20
Chemistry: "brain," 55
Chemoreceptor stimulation, 46
p-Chloramphetamine, 89

p-Chlorophenylalanine, 26, 76, 90
Chlorpromazine, 23, 76
  as antihallucinogen, 89
  carcinoid flush and, 108
  carcinoid tumors and, 89
  effect of, 88
Chromatography: of indoles, 20
Chromobacterium violaceum, 24
Ciliary activity: nerve stimulation
    and serotonin, 64
Circadian rhythm: and serotonin, 70-
    72
Circulation regulation: and seroto-
    nin, 96
Cocaine, 61
Compound 48/80, 33, 34
Connective tissue: and serotonin, 32-
    33
Cyproheptadine, 89

D

Depression: and tryptophan, 81
Deseril, 86
  structural formula, 87
Desipramine, 80
Determination methods: for seroto-
    nin, 20-21
Diethyldithiocarbamate, 58
3,4-Dihydroxy-alpha-methyl-phenyl-
    alanine, 24
3,4-Dihydroxyphenylalanine: and vas-
    omotor activity, 49
N,N-Dimethyltryptamine, 81
  cerebral actions of, 24
Discovery: changing atmosphere of,
    10-11
Distribution: of a chemical, 15-20
Dopa decarboxylase, 22
Dopamine
  kinetics and, steady-state, 75
  LSD and, 86
Dopamine-beta-oxidase inhibitor, 58
Down's syndrome: and serotonin, 111
Dumping syndrome: and serotonin,
    109-110

E

Edema
  anaphylactoid, 93
  histamine and, 33